ELECTRICAL CIRCUITS WITH VARIABLE PARAMETERS

including

PULSED-CONTROL SYSTEMS

by

V. A. TAFT

Translated by

F. IMMIRZI

Translation edited by

R. C. GLASS

A Pergamon Press Book

THE MACMILLAN COMPANY

NEW YORK

1964

THE MACMILLAN COMPANY
60 Fifth Avenue
New York 11, N.Y.

This book is distributed by
THE MACMILLAN COMPANY
pursuant to a special arrangement with
PERGAMON PRESS LIMITED
Oxford, England

Library of Congress Catalog Card Number 63-10036

This is a translation of the original Russian *Voprosy teorii elektricheskikh tsepei s peremennymi parametrami i sin eza impulsnykh i tsifrovykh avtomaticheskikh regulyatorov*, published in Moscow, 1960, by Izdatel'stvo Akademii nauk SSSR

MADE IN GREAT BRITAIN

CONTENTS

PREFACE

The results outlined in this work enable us to extend the frequency-analysis and operational methods to circuits with variable parameters. In addition, these results lend themselves in a number of cases to further development in connection with non-linear circuits.

As the work is intended primarily for engineers, several mathematical details have been omitted. The reader can find these details in other publications.

The author will be grateful for all observations. These are to be addressed to the Natsional'nyi Komitet I.F.A.C., Kalanchevskaya ulitsa, Moscow.

V. A. Taft

INTRODUCTION

The theory of circuits with variable parameters is of great value in a number of important engineering problems, both directly and in the study of periodic modes of operation of non-linear systems.

Problems involving the consideration of circuits with variable parameters occur, in particular, in electrical and radio engineering in the study of parametric oscillators, in the investigation of processes occurring in synchronous machines, in the investigation of parametric oscillations in non-linear circuits fed by a sinusoidal voltage, in the study of oscillation generators and also in the solution of the problem of frequency stabilization, in the design of parametric amplifiers and trigger circuits etc.

The theory of circuits with variable parameters is of great importance in the theory of automatic control. Not only are a number of important devices to be controlled, themselves systems with variable parameters, but pulse and digital control systems are also essentially systems with variable parameters. The latter systems are finding wider and wider application today, owing to the rapid development of digital techniques and the great possibilities opened up by their use.

We should mention that, in spite of the fact that the analysis of pulsed-control systems for the general case (when the equipment to be controlled has variable parameters) as well as the analysis of periodic modes of operation are both very important and urgent problems, considerable gaps exist in the theory at present.

In particular, in the investigation of periodic modes of operation the problem[3] of whether the frequency-analysis approach may be used for the study of their stability still remains to be clarified.

The investigation of the stability of periodic modes of operation reduces to the investigation of the stability of the solutions of differential equations with periodic coefficients. Much attention has been devoted to this problem, but no rigorous solution for the general case is known. Attempts have been made comparatively recently to use, for the solution of this problem, certain graphical methods based on the frequency-analysis approach.[1,2]

In particular, the problem, formulated by M.A. Aizerman,[3] of obtaining an approximate solution, based on the assumption of the presence in the system investigated of a linear element having the properties of an ideal filter, has been considered previously.[4] Such an approximate solution, however, does not enable one to obtain directly an answer to the problem of calculating the actual, non-idealized, frequency characteristic of the linear part of the system.

A rigorous solution of the problem is given in this work without any assumption as to the presence of an ideal filter.[6]

The solution of the problem reduces to giving to the characteristic equation of a system of equations with periodically varying coefficients, written down initially in the form of an infinite determinant, a finite form, by using a method analogous to the one used in deriving Hill's equation.

Firstly a system is considered with many degrees of freedom with one non-linear parameter and a method is given for reducing the characteristic equation for the equations of the small deviations from a periodic motion to a finite form. After the characteristic equation has been reduced to a finite form, known frequency-analysis criteria can be used for the analysis of stability. As is shown in this monograph, the method described can be extended to the case of several equations with periodic coefficients. The results obtained can be used in the solution of the engineering problems mentioned above.

A very convenient method in the theory of pulsed and digital control, enabling one to analyse a control system rapidly and clearly or to synthetize it, i.e. to determine the pulse characteristic of the transfer coefficient or alternatively the program in a digital controller, is the z-transformation method. In the case, however, when the system to be controlled is a system with variable parameters, the use of the z-transformation methods involves considerable difficulties. These difficulties are connected with the fact that, in order to determine the z-transform of a circuit with variable parameters, it is necessary to know the circuit response to an applied disturbance, or else the L-transform of this response. In order to determine the response by the usual methods, it is necessary to solve a differential equation with variable coefficients.[15] In the case of systems with variable parameters there are considerable difficulties also in determining the L-transform, the difficulties being connected with the use of operational methods in the solution of this problem, since in these circuits, in contrast to the case of circuits with constant parameters, one cannot isolate the system function in a closed form. For example, instead of the usual relation for a quadrupole with constant parameters $U_2(p) = U_1(p)K(p)$, more complex relations occur of the form $U_2(p) = F[U_1(p) \cdot K_i(p)]$ where $K_i(p)$ are the transfer coefficients of individual elements of the system and F is a functional dependence which in the general case can be very complicated.

In order to introduce a function equivalent, to some extent, to the system function of a circuit with constant parameters, the transient response to a unit impulse function is considered.

Bearing in mind that the transform of the δ-function is equal to unity, in the expression for the response to a δ-function input there only occur the values of the parameters of the system. The determination of this response, however, also gives rise in the general case, to considerable analytical difficulties.[19]

In particular, the L-transform of this response for systems with periodically or exponentially varying parameters can be expressed by means of infinite determinants. Complicated expressions of this type do not enable one to pass directly to the z-transforms.

A method is indicated in this work which enables one to pass from the expression of the L-transform of the response indicated, in the form of the ratio of two infinite determinants, to finite transcendental functions of the operator p, which enables one to reduce the theory of circuits with variable parameters to a form, similar to the theory of transmission lines. The relations obtained enable one to pass to the z-transforms, and the extension of the z-transformation methods to systems with variable parameters becomes possible.

In addition to the indicated extension of z-transformation theory, the analysis of pulsed and digital systems on the basis of the theory of circuits with variable parameters affords a deeper understanding of the properties of pulse and digital automatic-control systems, which in the general case are by their very nature systems with variable parameters.

Alongside with the extension of z-transformation theory, based on the direct evaluation of the L-transform of the response of a system to a δ-function input, we can carry out this extension by using the method of Fourier series (the method of reduction to steady-state modes of operation) in those cases when what matters is the behaviour of the system during a finite interval of time.[11, 12, 5] A sufficiently effective general method of solution of the problem can be obtained for the case of a finite interval.

The monograph comprises six chapters.

The first chapter considers the response of a circuit with periodically varying parameters (namely a periodically varying inductance; the method employed is however, also applicable to the general case when all parameters are periodically varying). Firstly a simple resonant circuit having a sinusoidally varying inductance and fed by a sinusoidal e.m.f. is investigated, and more complex cases are then examined when the variable parameter varies according to an arbitrary periodic law and the applied e.m.f. varies periodically. The latter case corresponds to the experimental method of determining a frequency characteristic.[7] In the same chapter the case of a complex circuit with many periodically varying parameters is also considered.

In the second chapter the free oscillations of a system with periodically varying parameters are investigated. A method is given for reducing the characteristic equation, written in the form of an infinite determinant, to a finite form. It is shown how it is possible to extend the results obtained to systems with monotonically varying parameters by replacing the assigned time-dependence of the parameters approximately by the sum of exponential functions.

The third chapter is devoted to the problem of the application of the operational calculus to circuits with variable parameters. The transform of the response of a circuit with periodically or exponentially varying parameters to a δ-function input is obtained here in a finite form, as well as an expression for the response of such a system to an arbitrary disturbance.

The principles and foundations of the calculation of the transients in circuits with constant and variable parameters by means of the Fourier-series method are treated in the fourth chapter.

The fifth chapter is devoted to the theory of pulsed systems, these being a particular case of systems with periodically varying parameters. First the basic principles of the methods for the analysis and synthesis of these systems on the basis of the z-transformation are outlined,[10, 16, 18, 19] and then, on the basis of the material expounded in the third and fourth chapters, it is shown how the method can be extended to the case of systems with variable parameters.

The sixth chapter is devoted to investigating the stability of circuits with variable parameters. Frequency-analysis methods for the investigation of the stability of automatic-control systems containing variable parameters are given.

CHAPTER I

THE FORCED CURRENT COMPONENT IN AN OSCILLATORY CIRCUIT WITH A PERIODICALLY VARYING INDUCTANCE

LET us consider the forced oscillations in a simple oscillatory circuit with a periodically varying inductance L, a constant resistance r and a capacitance C (Fig. 1).

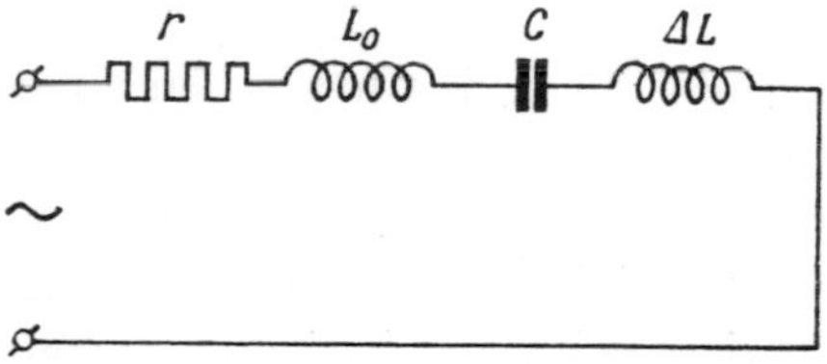

FIG. 1. Simple resonant circuit

If the inductance L were also a constant quantity, then, after connecting to the circuit a source of sinusoidal e.m.f. of frequency ω_0 oscillations would arise in the system of the same frequency. Resonance is possible in this circuit (for $r=0$) only when the frequency ω_0 of the e.m.f. source coincides with the frequency of free oscillations $\omega = 1/\sqrt{(LC)}$.

If the inductance L is not a constant quantity but a periodic function of time, the forced oscillations and the resonance phenomena occurring in such a circuit have a number of typical features. As will be seen below, these features are connected with the fact that, owing to the periodic variation of the parameters, the applied e.m.f., the frequency of which is ω_0, gives rise here to an infinite number of harmonic oscillations with combination frequencies $\omega_0+k\Omega$, where $k = -\infty, \ldots, -1, 0, 1, \ldots, \infty$, each of which can cause the occurence of resonance phenomena.

Let the inductance vary according to the relation

$$L(t) = L_0[1+m\cos(\Omega t+\alpha)], \tag{1.1}$$

where Ω is the frequency of variation of the parameter L, and m is the modulation depth.

Suppose that, in addition, the electromotive force of the source varies according to the relation

$$u(t) = U\cos(\omega_0 t+\theta_0) = \\ = \frac{U}{2}[e^{j(\omega_0 t+\theta_0)}+e^{-j(\omega_0 t+\theta_0)}], \tag{1.2}$$

where U is the amplitude, ω_0 is the angular frequency and θ_0 is the initial phase.

In this case the forced current component in the circuit (Fig. 1) will be determined as a particular solution of a linear differential equation with periodically varying coefficients

$$\frac{d}{dt}[L(t)\cdot i(t)]+r\cdot i(t)+\frac{1}{C}\int i(t)dt = u(t) \tag{1.3}$$

or

$$L(t)\frac{di(t)}{dt}+\left[r+\frac{dL(t))}{dt}\right]i(t)+\frac{1}{C}\int i(t)dt = u(t). \tag{1.4}$$

In the equations (1.3) and (1.4) $L(t)$ is a function of time defined by the expression (1.1).

We shall seek a particular solution of equation (1.3) in the form of the sum of the terms of a Fourier series

$$i(t) = \sum_{k=-\infty}^{\infty} I_k\cos[(\omega_0+k\Omega)t+\varphi_k]; \tag{1.5}$$

$$i(t) = \frac{1}{2} e^{j\omega_0 t} \sum_{k=-\infty}^{\infty} \dot{I}_k e^{jk\Omega t} + $$

$$+\frac{1}{2} e^{-j\omega_0 t} \sum_{k=-\infty}^{\infty} \dot{I}_{-k} e^{-jk\Omega t}, \tag{1.6}$$

where

$$\dot{I}_k = I_k e^{j\varphi k}; \quad \dot{I}_{-k} = I_k e^{-j\varphi k}. \tag{1.7}$$

We observe that $\dot{I}_k$ and $\dot{I}_{-k}$ are two complex conjugate numbers. In connexion with this we shall consider below the first term only of (1.6) and accordingly shall seek a solution of (1.3) in the form of the real part of the first term of (1.6). Since, according to (1.1),

$$L(t) = L_0\left(1+m\frac{e^{j(\Omega t+\alpha)}+e^{-j(\Omega t+\alpha)}}{2}\right),$$

then

$$[L(t)\cdot i(t)] = \mathrm{Re} L_0\left[\sum_{k=-\infty}^{\infty} \dot{I}_k e^{j(\omega_0+k\Omega)t} + \right.$$

$$\left. +\frac{m}{2}\sum_{k=-\infty}^{\infty} \dot{I}_k e^{j\{[\omega_0+(k+1)\Omega]t+\alpha\}} + \frac{m}{2}\sum_{k=-\infty}^{\infty} \dot{I}_k e^{j\{[\omega_0+(k-1)\Omega]t-\alpha\}}\right]. \tag{1.8}$$

In the second and third sums on replacing the index k by k' and k'' respectively according to the relations

$$k' = k+1; \qquad k'' = k-1; \tag{1.9}$$

we have

$$L(t)\cdot i(t) = \mathrm{Re} L_0 \sum_{k=-\infty}^{\infty}\left(\dot{I}_k + \frac{\dot{m}}{2}\dot{I}_{k-1} + \frac{\overset{*}{m}}{2}\dot{I}_{k+1}\right) e^{j(\omega_0+k\Omega)t}, \tag{1.10}$$

where $\dot{m} = me^{j\alpha}$, $\overset{*}{m} = me^{-j\alpha}$ and $\dot{I}_k$ is the complex amplitude of the current oscillation of frequency $e^{j(\omega_0+k\Omega)t}$. By substituting in (1.3) the expression for the current in the form of the first sum of (1.6) and the expression (1.10) for $L(t)\cdot i(t)$, we obtain

$$\sum_{k=-\infty}^{\infty}\left\{\left[j(\omega_0+k\Omega)L_0+r+\frac{1}{j(\omega_0+k\Omega)C}\right]\dot{I}_k+\right.$$

$$\left.+j(\omega_0+k\Omega)L_0\left(\frac{\dot{m}}{2}\dot{I}_{k-1}+\frac{\overset{*}{m}}{2}\dot{I}_{k+1}\right)\right\}e^{j(\omega_0+k\Omega)t} = Ue^{j(\omega_0 t+\theta_0)}. \quad (1.11)$$

Since equation (1.11) must be satisfied for arbitrary values of t, it is resolved into an infinite number of recurrent equations of the following form

$$\frac{m}{2}jL_0\dot{I}_{k-1}+\left(jL_0+\frac{r}{\omega_0+k\Omega}+\frac{1}{j(\omega_0+k\Omega)^2C}\right)\dot{I}_k+$$

$$+\frac{m}{2}jL_0\dot{I}_{k+1}=\frac{\dot{U}(k)}{\omega_0+k\Omega},\ k=(-\infty,\dots,-1,0,1,\dots,\infty) \quad (1.12)$$

where

$$\dot{U}(0) = U_m e^{j\theta_0};\ U(k) = 0 \text{ for } k \neq 0.$$

Let us consider now a particular case, which is very important in what follows. Let

$$\Omega = n\omega_0, \quad (1.13)$$

where n is an integral number. In this case equation (1.8) takes the following form

$$L(t)\cdot i(t) = \mathrm{Re}L_0\left[\sum_{k=-\infty}^{\infty}\dot{I}_k\cdot e^{j(1+kn)\omega_0 t}+\right.$$

$$\left.+\frac{\dot{m}}{2}\sum_{k=-\infty}^{\infty}\dot{I}_k\cdot e^{j[1+(k+1)n]\omega_0 t}+\frac{\overset{*}{m}}{2}\sum_{k=-\infty}^{\infty}\dot{I}_k\cdot e^{j[1+(k-1)n]\omega_0 t}\right]. \quad (1.14)$$

In equation (1.14) $\dot{I}_k$ in the first sum is the complex amplitude of the oscillation of frequency $(1+kn)\omega_0$, in the second sum is the complex amplitude of the oscillation of frequency $[1+(k+1)n]\omega_0$, and in the third sum is the complex amplitude of the oscillation of frequency $[1+(k-1)]n\omega_0$. Let us introduce a new notation in the indices in the second and third sums of

(1.14) by substituting $k'n$ for $(k+1)n$ in the second sum and $k''n$ for $(k-1)n$ in the third sum. Having introduced this new notation in the indices in the second and third sum we must replace the suffixes of the complex amplitudes as follows: k by $k-1$ in the second sum and k by $k+1$ in the third sum.

We then obtain from (1.14) after the transformations indicated

$$L(t)\cdot i(t) = \mathrm{Re} L_0 \sum_{k=-\infty}^{\infty} \left(\dot{I}_k + \frac{m}{2} \dot{I}_{k-1} + \frac{\overset{*}{m}}{2} I_{k+1} \right) e^{j(kn+1)\omega_0}. \tag{1.15}$$

Let us agree in this case to attribute to the complex amplitudes suffices corresponding to the frequency of the oscillation which has the given complex amplitude.

We thus obtain instead of (1.11)

$$\sum_{k=-\infty}^{\infty} \left\{ \left[j(kn+1)\omega_0 L_0 + r + \frac{1}{j(kn+1)\omega_0 C} \right] \dot{I}_{kn+1} + \right.$$

$$\left. + j(kn+1)\omega_0 L_0 \left(\frac{\dot{m}}{2} \dot{I}_{(k-1)n+1} + \frac{\overset{*}{m}}{2} \dot{I}_{(k+1)n+1} \right) \right\} e^{j(kn+1)\omega_0 t} =$$

$$= U e^{j(\omega_0 t + \theta_0)}. \tag{1.16}$$

The equations (1.16) are an infinite system of recurrent equations, from which the complex amplitudes can be determined.

These equations yield an infinite number of equations of the form

$$\frac{\dot{m}}{2} j\omega_0 L_0 \dot{I}_{(k-1)n+1} + \left(j\omega_0 L_0 + \frac{r}{kn+1} + \frac{1}{(kn+1)^2 \omega_0 C} \right) \dot{I}_{kn+1} +$$

$$+ \frac{\overset{*}{m}}{2} j\omega_0 L_0 \dot{I}_{(k+1)n+1} = \frac{\dot{U}(k)}{kn+1}, \; (k = -\infty, \ldots, -1, 0, 1, \ldots, \infty),$$

where

$$U(0) = \dot{U}; \quad \dot{U}(k) = 0 \text{ for } k \neq 0. \tag{1.17}$$

The equations (1.17) also represent an infinite system of recurrent equations.

Let us rewrite in full the equations (1.12) and (1.17). The system (1.12) will then take the following form

. . . .

$$\left.\begin{aligned} &\frac{m}{2} jL_0\dot{I}_{-2}+\left(jL_0+\frac{r}{\omega_0-\Omega}+\frac{1}{j(\omega_0-\Omega)^2C}\right)\dot{I}_{-1}+ \\ &\qquad +\frac{\overset{*}{m}}{2} jL_0\dot{I}_0 = 0; \\ &\frac{m}{2} jL_0\dot{I}_{-1}+\left(jL_0+\frac{r}{\omega_0}+\frac{1}{j\omega_0^2C}\right)\dot{I}_0+ \\ &\qquad +\frac{\overset{*}{m}}{2} jL_0\dot{I}_1 = \frac{\dot{U}(0)}{\omega_0}; \\ &\frac{m}{2} jL_0\dot{I}_0+\left(jL_0+\frac{r}{\omega_0+\Omega}+\frac{1}{j(\omega_0+\Omega)^2C}\right)\dot{I}_1+ \\ &\qquad +\frac{\overset{*}{m}}{2} jL_0\dot{I}_2 = 0, \end{aligned}\right\} \quad (1.18)$$

. . . .

where the suffix 1 of the complex amplitude denotes that this complex amplitude corresponds to an oscillation of frequency $(\omega_0+\Omega)$, the suffix 2 indicates that it corresponds to an oscillation of frequency $(\omega_0+2\Omega)$ etc.

Similarly the system of equations (1.17) written in full will have the form

. . . .

$$\begin{aligned} &\frac{\dot{m}}{2} j\omega_0L_0\dot{I}_{1-2n}+\left(j\omega_0L_0+\frac{r}{1-n}+\frac{1}{j(1-n)^2\omega_0C}\right)\dot{I}_{1-n}+ \\ &\qquad +\frac{\overset{*}{m}}{2} j\omega_0L_0\dot{I}_1 = 0; \\ &\frac{\dot{m}}{2} j\omega_0L_0\dot{I}_{1-n}+\left(j\omega_0L_0+r+\frac{1}{j\omega_0C}\right)\dot{I}_1+ \\ &\qquad +\frac{\overset{*}{m}}{2} j\omega_0L_0\dot{I}_{1+n} = \dot{U}(0); \end{aligned}$$

$$\frac{\dot{m}}{2}j\omega_0 L_0 \dot{I}_1 + \left(j\omega_0 L_0 + \frac{r}{1+n} + \frac{1}{j(1+n)^2\omega_0 C}\right)\dot{I}_{1+n} +$$

$$+\frac{\overset{*}{m}}{2}j\omega_0 L_0 \dot{I}_{1+2n} = 0, \tag{1.19}$$

. . . .

where the index $1+n$ of the complex amplitude indicates that this complex amplitude corresponds to an oscillation of frequency $(1+n)\omega_0$, the suffix $(1+2n)$ corresponds to the oscillation of frequency $(1+2n)\omega_0$ etc.

It follows from what has been said that a sinusoidal voltage of frequency ω_0 causes in an oscillatory circuit with a sinusoidally varying inductance forced oscillations with combination frequencies

$$\omega_k = |\,\omega_0 \pm k\Omega\,|, \tag{1.20}$$

where $k = 0, 1, 2, \ldots, \infty$.

In the particular case when the frequency of the forced oscillations ω_0 and the frequency of variation of the parameter, Ω, are connected with each other by the relation $\Omega = n\omega_0$, forced oscillations will occur with the combination frequencies

$$\omega_k = \omega_0\,|\,1 \pm kn\,|, \tag{1.21}$$

where $k = 0, 1, 2, \ldots, \infty$.

It can be shown that in the particular case when $n = 2$ or $n = 1$, the infinite system of equations (1.18) or (1.19) reduces to two independent semi-infinite systems. The independent variables that occur in these systems are complex conjugate quantities.

In fact, if $n = \Omega/\omega_0 = 2$, i.e. $\Omega = 2\omega_0$ the frequency corresponding to the complex amplitude $\dot{I}_{-1}$ in the system of equations (1.18) is equal to $-\omega_0$, i.e. the vectors $\dot{I}_{-1}$ and $\dot{I}_0$ are complex conjugate vectors. Correspondingly also the right-hand sides of those equations of the system in the central term of which there occur respectively the complex amplitude $\dot{I}_0$ and $\overset{*}{I}_{-1}$ are complex conjugate quantities. Rewriting these two equations of the system (1.18) for the particular case considered, we obtain

$$\left.\begin{aligned} -\frac{m}{2}j\omega_0 L_0 \overset{*}{\dot{I}}_1 + \left(-j\omega_0 L_0 + r + \frac{1}{-j\omega_0 C}\right)\overset{*}{\dot{I}}_0 - \\ -\frac{m}{2}j\omega_0 L_0 \dot{I}_0 = \frac{\overset{*}{\dot{U}}m}{2}; \\ \frac{m}{2}j\omega_0 L_0 \overset{*}{\dot{I}}_0 + \left(j\omega_0 L_0 + r + \frac{1}{j\omega_0 C}\right)\dot{I}_0 + \\ +\frac{m}{2}j\omega_0 L_0 \dot{I}_1 = \frac{\dot{U}m}{2}. \end{aligned}\right\} \quad (1.18a)$$

The first and second equations of the system (1.18a) are complex conjugate. On passing from the complex quantities to their real parts and bearing in mind that the real parts of complex conjugate quantities are equal to each other, it is easily verified that the infinite system of equations (1.18) reduces to two equal systems.

The infinite system of equations can be similarly reduced in the case when $\Omega = \omega_0$. In fact, rewriting the system of equations (1.18), we obtain for this case

$$\left.\begin{aligned} -\frac{m}{2}j\omega_0 L_0 \dot{I}_{-3} + \left(-j\omega_0 L_0 + r + \frac{1}{-j\omega_0 C}\right)\dot{I}_{-2} - \\ -\frac{m}{2}j\omega_0 L_0 \dot{I}_{-1} = \overset{*}{\dot{U}}_m; \\ \frac{m}{2}\cdot j0\cdot L_0 \dot{I}_{-2} + \left(j0\cdot L_0 + r + \frac{1}{j0\cdot C}\right)\dot{I}_{-1} + \\ +\frac{m}{2}j0 L_0 \dot{I}_0 = 0; \\ \frac{m}{2}j\omega_0 L_0 \dot{I}_{-1} + \left(j\omega_0 L_0 + r + \frac{1}{j\omega_0 C}\right)\dot{I}_0 + \\ +\frac{m}{2}j\omega_0 L_0 \dot{I}_1 = \dot{U}_m. \end{aligned}\right\} \quad (1.18b)$$

As can be seen from the system (1.18b) $\dot{I}_{-1} = 0$ and the remaining two equations are complex conjugate.

Other special cases corresponding to various values of n can be analysed in a similar manner.

It is of interest for what follows to consider the more general case, namely the case of an arbitrary periodic external e.m.f. Let the applied voltage be equal to

$$u(t) = \mathrm{Re} \sum_{s=1}^{\infty} U_s e^{j(s\omega_0 t + \theta_{0s})}, \tag{1.22}$$

where ω_0 is the angular frequency of the fundamental harmonic of the voltage applied.

As in the preceding case we shall seek, for the s-th harmonic of the applied voltage, a particular solution of the equation (1.3) in the form

$$i_s(t) = \sum_{k=-\infty}^{\infty} I_{sk} \cdot \cos\left[(s\omega_0 + k\Omega)t + \psi_{sk}\right] \tag{1.23}$$

A particular solution of equation (1.3) when all harmonic components are applied will accordingly have the form

$$i(t) = \sum_{s=1}^{\infty} i_s(t) = \sum_{s=1}^{\infty} \sum_{k=-\infty}^{\infty} I_{sk} \cdot \cos\left[(s\omega_0 + k\Omega)t + \psi_{sk}\right]. \tag{1.24}$$

The determination of the amplitudes $\dot{I}_{sk}$ must be carried out here for each of the harmonics of the applied voltage separately. This determination for each of the harmonics is carried out in the same manner as for the case of a sinusoidal applied voltage considered above.

The determination of the complex amplitudes is considerably simplified in the case when the angular frequency and the frequency of variation of the inductance are connected with each other by the relation (1.13). In this case expression (1.24) takes the following form

$$i(t) = \sum_{s=1}^{\infty} \sum_{k=-\infty}^{\infty} I_{s+kn} \cos\left[(s + kn)\omega_0 t + \psi_{sk}\right]. \tag{1.25}$$

We obtain as for (1.15),†

$$L(t)\cdot i(t) = \mathrm{Re} L_0 \sum_{s=1}^{\infty} \sum_{k=-\infty}^{\infty} \left(\dot{I}_{kn+s} + \frac{m}{2} \dot{I}_{(k-1)n+s} + \right.$$

$$\left. + \frac{\overset{*}{m}}{2} \dot{I}_{(k+1)n+s} \right). \tag{1.26}$$

Here, just as in (1.16), we introduce such a notation for the suffixes of the complex amplitudes that they be equal to the value of the frequency of that oscillation to which the given complex amplitude corresponds.

After substituting (1.25) and (1.26) in (1.3) we obtain

$$\sum_{s=1}^{\infty} \sum_{k=-\infty}^{\infty} \left\{ \left[j(s+kn)\omega_0 L_0 + r + \frac{1}{j(s+kn)\omega_0 C} \right] \dot{I}_{kn+s} + \right.$$

$$\left. + j(s+kn)\omega_0 L_0 \left(\frac{m}{2} \dot{I}_{(k+1)n+s} + \dot{I}_{(k-1)n+s} \right) \right\} e^{j(s+kn)\omega_0 t} =$$

$$= \sum_{s=1}^{\infty} \dot{U}_s e^{js\omega_0 t}. \tag{1.27}$$

The equation (1.27) reduces to n systems of equations of the form

$$\frac{m}{2} j\omega_0 L_0 \dot{I}_{(k-1)n+s} + \left(j\omega_0 L_0 + \frac{r}{kn+s} + \frac{1}{j(kn+s)^2 C} \right) \dot{I}_{kn+s} +$$

$$+ \frac{\overset{*}{m}}{2} j\omega_0 L_0 \dot{I}_{(k+1)n+s} = \frac{\dot{U}_{kn+s}}{kn+s} \tag{1.28}$$

$$(k = -\infty, \ldots, -1, 0, 1, \ldots, \infty).$$

† The expression (1.25) can be represented, similarly to (1.5) in the form

$$\frac{1}{2} \sum_{s=1}^{\infty} e^{js\omega_0 t} \sum_{k=-\infty}^{\infty} \dot{I}_k e^{jkn\omega_0 t} + \frac{1}{2} \sum_{s=1}^{\infty} e^{-js\omega_0 t} \sum_{k=-\infty}^{\infty} \dot{I}_{-k} e^{-jkn\omega_0 t}. \tag{1.6a}$$

Here, just as above, only the first term is considered. Accordingly also the sum on the right-hand side will be taken from $s = 1$ to $s = \infty$ only.

The equations (1.28) represent for a given value of s an infinite system of recurrent equations from which the complex amplitudes of all harmonics of the required current caused by the $(s+kn)$-th harmonics of the applied voltage can be determined.

Since the amplitude of the s-th harmonic of current is connected with the amplitudes of only the $(s-n)$-th and $(s+n)$-th harmonics, the system (1.27) reduces, as has been indicated, to n independent infinite systems of equations corresponding to the values

$$s = 1,\ 2,\ 3, \ldots, (n-1),\ n.$$

The first of these systems corresponding to the value $s = 1$ contains the amplitudes

$$\ldots, \dot{I}_{1-2n}, \dot{I}_{1-n}, \dot{I}_1\ \dot{I}_{1+n}, \dot{I}_{1+2n}, \ldots .$$

the second, corresponding to the value $s = 2$, contains

$$\ldots, \dot{I}_{2-2n}, \dot{I}_{2-n}, \dot{I}_2, \dot{I}_{2+n}, \dot{I}_{2+2n}, \ldots;$$

the third, corresponding to the value $s = 3$, contains

$$\ldots, \dot{I}_{3-2n}, \dot{I}_{3-n}, \dot{I}_3, \dot{I}_{3+n}, \dot{I}_{3+2n}, \ldots;$$

and the n-th system contains the amplitudes

$$\ldots, \dot{I}_{-2n}, \dot{I}_{-n}, \dot{I}_0, \dot{I}_n, \dot{I}_{2n}, \ldots .$$

We observe that all pairs of complex amplitudes the suffixes of which differ in their sign are complex conjugate numbers.

The determinants made up of the coefficients of the unknown complex amplitudes, occurring in each of the enumerated independent systems, are different from zero. Therefore all complex amplitudes occuring in the second, third etc. up to and including the n-th system of equations will be identically equal to zero if their right-hand sides are equal to zero.

We observe here that a part of these infinite systems can be excluded from the analysis. In particular the system of equations corresponding to $s = 1$ will contain the complex amplitudes of the oscillations of the same frequencies as the system corresponding to the value $s=n-1$. In fact the coefficients of the system of equations corresponding to $s=n-1$ are complex conjugate quantities with respect to the coefficients of the system corresponding to $s=1$. The same occurs also for the systems corresponding to $s=k$ and $s=n-k$ etc.

The infinite system of recurrent equations corresponding to $s=1$ can be written in full in the following manner

. . . .

$$\frac{m}{2} j\omega_0 L_0 \dot{I}_{1-2n} + \left(j\omega_0 L_0 + \frac{r}{1-n} + \frac{1}{j(1-n)^2\omega_0 C} \right) \dot{I}_{1-n} + + \frac{\overset{*}{m}}{2} j\omega_0 L_0 \dot{I}_1 = \frac{\dot{U}(-1)}{1-n};$$

$$\frac{\dot{m}}{2} j\omega_0 L_0 \dot{I}_{1-n} + \left(j\omega_0 L_0 + r + \frac{1}{j\omega_0 C} \right) \dot{I}_1 + + \frac{\overset{*}{m}}{2} j\omega_0 L_0 \dot{I}_{1+n} = \dot{U}(0);$$

$$\frac{\dot{m}}{2} j\omega_0 L_0 \dot{I}_1 + \left(j\omega_0 L_0 + \frac{r}{1+n} + \frac{1}{j(1+n)^2\omega_0 C} \right) \dot{I}_{1+n} + + \frac{\overset{*}{m}}{2} j\omega_0 L_0 \dot{I}_{1+2n} = \dot{U}(1)/(1+n). \qquad (1.29)$$

. . . .

In the system of equations (1.29), in contrast to (1.18) and (1.19), the right-hand sides are different from zero, for non-zero values of k also. That is, every harmonic component of frequency $(s+kn)\omega_0$, where s and k are assigned, is generated here by all components of the applied voltage of frequency $(s+kn)\omega_0$ where s is the same and $k=1, \pm 2, \pm 3, \ldots, \pm \infty$.

For one or several values of k, it can happen that the phase shift between the current in the circuit and the electromotive force applied to the circuit will be larger than $\pm 90°$. When the value of the angle between the current of any frequency and the voltage component of the same frequency exceeds $\pm 90°$ the power for the corresponding harmonic becomes negative. This means that the circuit is a generator for the oscillations of the given frequency. The power released by the circuit at the frequency of the oscillations generated, is provided at the expense of the energy required for varying the parameter and of the energy of the oscillations of the other frequencies.

All the above considerations correspond to a simple resonant circuit the inductance of which varies according to a simple sinusoidal law.

In a similar manner we can also consider the more general case when the inductance varies according to an arbitrary periodic law

$$L(t) = 2l^{(0)} + 2L^{(1)} \cos(\Omega t + \alpha_1) + \ldots + 2L^{(r)} \cos(r\Omega t + \alpha_r) + \ldots,$$

where

$$L^{(0)} = 2l^{(0)}; \quad 2L^{(r)} = L_0 m_r \tag{1.30}$$

When the self-inductance coefficient varies according to (1.30) we obtain for the quantity $[L(t)\cdot i(t)]$

$$[L(t)\cdot i(t)] = \mathrm{Re} L^{(0)} \Bigg[\sum_{k=-\infty}^{\infty} \dot{I}_k e^{j(\omega_0 + k\Omega)t} + \frac{\dot{m}_1}{2} \sum_{k=-\infty}^{\infty} \dot{I}_k e^{j[\omega_0 + (k+1)\Omega]t} +$$

$$+ \frac{\overset{*}{m}_1}{2} \sum_{k=-\infty}^{\infty} \dot{I}_k e^{j[\omega_0 + (k-1)\Omega]t} + \ldots + \frac{\dot{m}_r}{2} \sum_{k=-\infty}^{\infty} \dot{I}_k e^{j[\omega_0 + (k+r)\Omega]t} +$$

$$+ \frac{\overset{*}{m}_r}{2} \sum_{k=-\infty}^{\infty} \dot{I}_k e^{j[\omega_0 + (k-r)\Omega]t} + \ldots, \Bigg],$$

where

$$\dot{m}_r = m_r e^{j\alpha r}; \quad \overset{*}{m}_r = m_r e^{-j\alpha r}. \tag{1.31}$$

By replacing the index k in the $(k+r)$-th and $(k-r)$-th sum by k' and k'' respectively according to the formulae

$$k' = (k+r); \; k'' = (k-r), \text{ where } \quad (r = 0, 1, \ldots, \infty),$$

we reduce (1.31) to the form

$$[L(t)\cdot i(t)] =$$
$$= \mathrm{Re} L^{(0)} \sum_{k=-\infty}^{\infty} \left[\dot{I}_k + \frac{\dot{m}_1}{2}\dot{I}_{k-1} + \frac{\overset{*}{\dot{m}}_1}{2}\dot{I}_{k+1} + \ldots + \frac{\dot{m}_r}{2}\dot{I}_{k-r} + \ldots \right]; \tag{1.32}$$

Accordingly we obtain for the oscillatory circuit the following system of equations

$$\sum_{k=-\infty}^{\infty} \left\{ \left[j(\omega_0 + k\Omega)L_0 + r + \frac{1}{j(\omega_0 + k\Omega)C} \right] \dot{I}_k + \right.$$
$$\left. + \sum_{r=0}^{\infty} (j\omega_0 + k\Omega) \left[\frac{\dot{m}_r}{2}\dot{I}_{k-r} + \frac{\overset{*}{\dot{m}}_r}{2}\dot{I}_{k+r} \right] \right\} =$$
$$= \sum_{k=-\infty}^{\infty} \left\{ \left[j(\omega_0 + k\Omega)L^{(0)} + r + \frac{1}{(j\omega_0 + k\Omega)C} \right] \dot{I}_k + \right.$$
$$\left. + \sum_{r=-\infty}^{\infty} j(\omega_0 + k\Omega)L^{(r)} \; \dot{I}_{(k-r)} \right\} = \dot{U}_k. \tag{1.33}$$

All that has been said above was valid for a simple resonant circuit, but the method is equally applicable to the case when the resonant circuit is connected in series with some complicated network the input impedance of which is Z_{in}.

In this case the resulting equations will have a form analogous to the equation for a simple oscillatory circuit, except for the fact that in the central term, along with the voltage drop across the inductance L the resistance r and the capacitance C, there will also occur a voltage drop across the external impedance Z_{in}.

Let us consider a network made up of N oscillatory circuits. Let there be in the ν-th circuit of this network an inductance varying periodically with the fundamental frequency Ω. Let an e.m.f.

$$\sum_{k=-\infty}^{\infty} U_k \cos(\omega_0 + k\Omega)t =$$
$$= \mathrm{Re} \sum_{k=-\infty}^{\infty} U_k e^{j(\omega_0 + k\Omega)t}, \tag{1.34}$$

be applied to the terminals of the ν-th circuit, ω_0 being the frequency of the applied disturbance and Ω the frequency of variation of the parameters.

The equations of the transient in this circuit have the following form†

$$p[L_{\nu\nu}(t)i_\nu(t)]+\sum_{s=1}^{N} M_{\nu s}(p)i_s(t) =$$

$$= \mathrm{Re}\sum_{k=-\infty}^{\infty} U_m e^{j(\omega_0+k\Omega)t}; \tag{1.35a}$$

$$\sum_{s=1}^{N} M_{\xi s}(p)i_s(t) = 0; \tag{1.35b}$$

$$(\xi = 1,\ 2,\ \ldots,\ \nu-1,\ \nu+1,\ \ldots,\ n),$$

where $M_{\nu s}$ and $M_{\xi s}$ are functions of the operator $p=d/dt$ of the form

$$M_{s\nu} = L_{s\nu}p+R_{s\nu}+\frac{1}{C_{s\nu}p}.$$

We can write for the dynamical inductance of the ν-th circuit in the general case [see (1.30)]

$$L_{\nu\nu}(t) = 2l_{\nu\nu}^{(0)}+2L_{\nu\nu}^{(1)}\cos(\Omega t+\alpha_1)+\ldots+$$
$$+2L_{\nu\nu}^{(r)}\cos(r\Omega t+\alpha_r)+\ldots=$$
$$=\frac{1}{2}\sum_{r=-\infty}^{\infty}\dot{L}_{\nu\nu}^{(r)}e^{j(r\Omega t+\alpha_r)},$$

where

$$L_{\nu\nu}^{(0)} = 2l_{\nu\nu}^{(0)};\ L_{\nu\nu}^{(r)}=\mu L_{\nu\nu}^{(r-1)}; \tag{1.36}$$

We shall seek a particular solution of (1.35) in the form

$$i_\xi(t) = \mathrm{Re}\, e^{j\omega_0 t}\sum_{k=-\infty}^{\infty} I_s^{(k)}e^{j(k\Omega t+\varphi_k)} =$$

$$= \mathrm{Re}\, e^{j\omega_0 t}\sum_{k=-\infty}^{\infty}\dot{I}_s^{(k)}e^{jk\Omega t}\quad(\xi = 1,\ 2,\ \ldots,\ \nu,\ \ldots,\ n). \tag{1.37}$$

† I.e., using the terminology of electrical engineering, we assume that the inductance or the capacitance is found in the corresponding main branch of the network.

In (1.35b) let us take all i_ν to the right-hand sides. We obtain, as a result, a system of (N-1) equations with respect to the currents i_s (for $s \neq \nu$). In the system of equations (1.35b) by expressing the currents i_s ($s \neq \nu$) in terms of the currents i_ν we obtain

$$i_s = \frac{\Delta_s}{\Delta} = \sum_{\xi-1}^{n} \zeta_{\nu s} \, \Delta \xi_s i_\nu \tag{1.38}$$

where Δ is the determinant of the system of equations obtained from (1.35*b*) after taking all i_ν to the right-hand sides, and Δ_s is the minor of the determinant Δ after cancelling the corresponding row and column.

On substituting in (1.35a) the values of i_s thus found we obtain

$$p[L_{\nu\nu}(t) i_\nu(t)] + \sum_{\substack{s=1 \\ s \neq \nu}}^{N} (M_{\nu\nu} + M_{\nu s} Z_{s\nu}) i_\nu(t) =$$

$$= \mathrm{Re} \sum_{k=-\infty}^{\infty} U_k e^{j(\omega_0 + k\Omega)t}.$$

or

$$p[L_{\nu\nu}(t) i_\nu(t)] + Z_{\nu\,\mathrm{in}} i_\nu(t) = \mathrm{Re} \sum_{k=-\infty}^{\infty} \dot{U}_k e^{j(\omega_0 + k\Omega)t}, \tag{1.39}$$

where $Z_{\nu\,\mathrm{in}}$ is the input impedance measured across the terminals of the variable inductance, connected in the main branch of the ν-th circuit.

By substituting in (1.39) $L_{\nu\nu}(t)$ and $i_\nu(t)$ according to (1.36) and (1.37) we obtain

$$\sum_{k=-\infty}^{\infty} \left\{ (j\omega_0 + jk\,\Omega) \left[L_{\nu\nu}^{(0)} + \frac{Z_{\nu\,\mathrm{in}}(j\omega_0 + jk\,\Omega)}{j\omega_0 + jk\,\Omega} \right] \dot{I}_\nu^{(k)} e^{(j\omega_0 + jk\Omega)t} \right\} +$$

$$+ \sum_{k=-\infty}^{\infty} \sum_{\substack{r=-\infty \\ r \neq 0}}^{\infty} [j\omega_0 + j(k+m)\,\Omega] \, \dot{L}_{\nu\nu}^{(r)} \, \dot{I}_\nu^{(k)} e^{[j\omega_0 + j(k+r)\Omega]t} =$$

$$= \sum_{k=-\infty}^{\infty} \frac{\dot{U}_k e^{j(\omega_0 + k\Omega)t}}{j(\omega + k\Omega)} \, . \tag{1.40}$$

After replacing $(k+m)$ by k in the second summation we obtain

$$\sum_{k=-\infty}^{\infty}\left\{(j\omega_0+jk\Omega)\left[\dot{L}_{\nu\nu}^{(0)}+\frac{Z_{\nu\,\mathrm{in}}(j\omega_0+jk\Omega)}{j\omega_0+jk\Omega}\right]\dot{I}_{\nu}^{(k)}e^{(j\omega_0+jk\Omega)t}\right\}+$$

$$+\sum_{k=-\infty}^{\infty}\sum_{\substack{r=-\infty\\ r\neq 0}}^{\infty}(j\omega_0+jk\Omega)L_{\nu\nu}^{(r)}\dot{I}_{\nu}^{(k-r)}\,e^{(j\omega_0+jk\Omega)t}=\sum_{k=-\infty}^{\infty}\frac{\dot{U}_{k}e^{j(\omega_0+k\Omega)t}}{j(\omega+k\alpha)}. \tag{1.41}$$

After equating to zero the coefficients of equal powers we obtain the system of equations

$$\left(L_{\nu\nu}^{(0)}+\frac{Z_{\nu\,\mathrm{in}}(j\omega_0+jk\Omega)}{j\omega_0+jk\Omega}\right)\dot{I}_{\nu}^{(k)}+$$

$$+\sum_{\substack{r=-\infty\\ r\neq 0}}^{\infty}L_{\nu\nu}^{(r)}\,\dot{I}_{\nu}^{(k-r)}=\sum_{k=-\infty}^{\infty}\frac{\dot{U}_k}{j(\omega_0+k\Omega)}e^{j(\omega_0+k\Omega)t}$$

$$(k=-\infty,\ldots,-1,0,1,\ldots,+\infty). \tag{1.42}$$

Let us consider in conclusion the more general case when there is a variable parameter $L(t)$ in b circuits, where $b < N$.

We can write in this case, instead of the system of equations (1.35),

$$p[L_{\nu\nu}(t)i_{\nu}(t)]+\sum_{s=1}^{b}M_{\nu s}(p)i_s(t)+\sum_{\xi=b+1}^{N}M_{\nu\xi}(p)i_{\xi}(t)=$$

$$=\mathrm{Re}\sum_{k=-\infty}^{+\infty}\dot{U}_{\nu k}e^{j(\omega_0+k\Omega)t};\qquad[\nu=1,2,\ldots,b]$$

$$\sum_{s=1}^{n}M_{\xi s}(p)i_s(t)=0;\quad[\xi=b+1;\ldots,N], \tag{1.43}$$

where N is the number of circuits, ν is the index of a circuit containing a variable inductance, ξ is the index of a circuit containing constant parameters only, s is an arbitrary index and $p=d/dt$.

Let us assume, in contrast to the case considered above, that the periodic functions $L_{\nu\nu}(t)$ can be represented in the form of a finite sum containing m_1 terms. Just as above, we shall seek a solution in the form (1.37).

By expressing all i_ξ in terms of i_ν and making all transformations carried out above in passing from (1.35) to (1.41) we obtain a system of b equations of the form†

$$\sum_{k=-\infty}^{\infty}(j\omega_0+jk\,\Omega)\left[L_{\nu\nu}^{(0)}+\frac{Z_{\nu\,\mathrm{in}}(j\omega_0+jk\,\Omega)}{j\omega_0+jk\,\Omega}\right]\dot{I}_\nu^{(k)}e^{(j\omega_0+jk\Omega)t}+$$

$$+\sum_{k=-\infty}^{\infty}\sum_{r=-\infty}^{m_1}[j(\omega_0+k\,\Omega)\,\dot{L}_{\nu\nu}^{(r)}\,\dot{I}_\nu^{(k-r)}\,e^{j(\omega_0+k\Omega)t}]+$$

$$+\sum_{k=-\infty}^{\infty}\sum_{\substack{s=1\\ s\neq\nu}}^{b}(j\omega_0+jk\,\Omega)M_{\nu s}(j\omega_0+jk\,\Omega)I_s^{(k)}e^{(j\omega_0+jk\Omega)t}=$$

$$=\dot{U}_{\nu k}e^{j(\omega_0+k\Omega)t},$$

$$(\nu=1,\ 2,\ \ldots,\ b). \qquad (1.44)$$

† We are assuming here, just as above, that the mutual elements $L_{\nu s}$, $r_{\nu s}$ and $C_{\nu s}$ are not functions of time. In the contrary case, an additional sum with respect to r for the currents $I_s^{(k-r)}$ occurs in the equation.

CHAPTER II

FREE OSCILLATIONS IN CIRCUITS WITH VARIABLE PARAMETERS

LET us now proceed to the analysis of free oscillations in circuits with variable parameters. We shall discuss firstly circuits with periodic parameters. Omitting from our considerations the problem of the physical origin of these oscillations, which problem has already been repeatedly considered, we shall derive relations determining the frequencies of these oscillations.

The frequencies of free oscillations can be found from the relations obtained above.

Let us discuss the particular case of a complex circuit with one periodically varying inductance. We shall obtain the equations of the free oscillations for this case by equating to zero the right-hand sides of the equations (1.42) of the preceding section and by replacing j^{ω_0} by λ in them. We obtain in this manner the following system of homogeneous equations

$$\left(L_{vv}^{(0)} + \frac{Z_{v\,\mathrm{in}}(\lambda + jk\Omega)}{\lambda + jk\Omega}\right)\dot{I}_v^{(k)} + \sum_{\substack{m=-\infty \\ m\neq 0}}^{\infty} L_{vv}^{(m)} \dot{I}_v^{(k-m)} = 0$$

$$(k = -\infty, \ldots, -1, 0, 1, \ldots, \infty). \qquad (2.1)$$

In the equation (2.1) the initial phase of the modulation of the parameter occurs implicitly, since $L_{vv}^{(m)} = L_{vv}^{(0)} e^{j\alpha}m$. If, however, we multiply all equations of the system (2.1) by $\exp(-jk\alpha)$ and introduce the notation $\dot{I}'_k = \dot{I}_k e^{-jk\alpha}$, then it can easily be seen that, for a sinusoidal variation of the parameter, the eigen-values λ_i do not depend on α_i.

As is well-known, in order that a system of homogeneous equations may have non-zero solutions, it is necessary and sufficient that its determinant be equal to zero. By equating to zero the determinant of the system (2.1) we can find the values of λ for which this condition is fulfilled. The values of λ thus found are the frequencies of free oscillations.

Let us consider in greater detail the general properties of these frequencies.

The determinant of the system (2.1) written down in full has the following form

$$\Delta(\lambda) = \begin{vmatrix} \ldots; L_{\nu\nu}^{(-1)}; \left(L_{\nu\nu}^{(0)} + \dfrac{Z_{\nu\,\mathrm{in}}}{\lambda - j\Omega}\right); L_{\nu\nu}^{(1)}; L_{\nu\nu}^{(2)}; \ldots \\ \ldots; L_{\nu\nu}^{(-2)}; L_{\nu\nu}^{(-1)}; \left(L_{\nu\nu}^{(0)} + \dfrac{Z_{\nu\,\mathrm{in}}}{\lambda}\right); L_{\nu\nu}^{(1)}; L_{\nu\nu}^{(2)}; \ldots \\ \ldots; L_{\nu\nu}^{(-2)}; L_{\nu\nu}^{(-1)}; \left(L_{\nu\nu}^{(0)} + \dfrac{Z_{\nu\,\mathrm{in}}}{\lambda + j\Omega}\right); L_{\nu\nu}^{(1)}; \ldots \end{vmatrix} = 0, \qquad (2.2)$$

As can be seen from (2.2) the determinant $\Delta(\lambda)$ satisfies the condition

$$\Delta(\lambda) = \Delta(\lambda + jk\Omega) \text{ where } k = 0,\ 1, 2, \ldots, \infty \qquad (2.3)$$

i.e. $\Delta(\lambda)$ is a periodic function of the frequency with period equal to Ω. It follows from this that if a number λ_i is a root of the equation $\Delta(\lambda) = 0$ then also $(\lambda_i + jk\Omega)$ is a root of (2.2) for any integer k. Thus the free oscillation of a system with periodically varying parameters contains an infinite number of harmonic components. The same follows from purely physical considerations.

It can be shown that the total number λ_i of different natural frequencies, differing from each other by a number which is not a multiple of Ω, is equal to the number of natural frequencies which will occur in the circuit considered when its parameters are constant.

In order to prove this proposition we shall reduce the characteristic equation represented in the form of the infinite determinant (2.2) to a finite form.

Such a transformation can be carried out on the basis of an extension of the theory of Hill-type equations.

Let us introduce the notation†

$$\frac{Z_{\nu\,\mathrm{in}}(\lambda+jk\Omega)}{\lambda+jk\Omega}=\frac{F_{1\,\mathrm{in}}(\lambda+jk\Omega)}{F_{2\,\mathrm{in}}(\lambda+jk\Omega)}\,. \tag{2.3a}$$

Substituting (2.3a) in (2.1) we obtain

$$[L_{\nu\nu}^{(0)}F_{2\,\mathrm{in}}(\lambda+jk\Omega)+F_{1\,\mathrm{in}}(\lambda+jk\Omega)]\dot{I}_{\nu}^{(k)}+$$
$$+\,F_{2\,\mathrm{in}}(\lambda+jk\Omega)\sum_{\substack{m=-\infty\\ m\neq 0}}^{m}L_{\nu\nu}^{(m)}\dot{I}_{\nu}^{(k-m)}=0$$
$$(k=-\infty,\,\ldots,\,-1,\,0,\,1,\,\ldots,\,\infty)$$

or

$$\left[1+\frac{L_{\nu\nu}^{(0)}F_{2\,\mathrm{in}}(\lambda+jk\Omega)}{F_{1\,\mathrm{in}}(\lambda+jk\Omega)}\right]\dot{I}_{\nu}^{(k)}+$$
$$+\,\frac{F_{2\,\mathrm{in}}(\lambda+jk\Omega)}{F_{1\,\mathrm{in}}(\lambda+jk\Omega)}\sum_{\substack{m=-\infty\\ m\neq 0}}^{m}L_{\nu\nu}^{(m)}I_{\nu}^{(k-m)}=0 \tag{2.4}$$
$$(k=-\infty,\,\ldots,\,-1,\,0,\,1\,\ldots,\,\infty).$$

Let us put $(\lambda+jk\Omega)=\nu_k$ and denote by $\alpha_1,\alpha_2,\ldots,\alpha_q$ the roots of the polynomial $F_{1\mathrm{in}}\,(\lambda+jk\Omega)=F_{1\mathrm{in}}\,(\nu_k)$; then (2.4) can be rewritten in the form

$$\left\{1+\sum_{i=1}^{n}\frac{A_{10}^{(i)}}{(\mu_k-\alpha_i)}+\sum_{i=1}^{n-r}\frac{A_{20}^{(i)}}{(\mu_k-\alpha_i)^2}+\sum_{i=1}^{n-r-t}\frac{A_{30}^{(i)}}{(\mu_k-\alpha_i)^3}+\ldots\right\}\dot{I}_{\nu}^{(h)}+$$
$$+\sum_{\substack{m=-\infty\\ m\neq 0}}^{\infty'}\left\{\sum_{i=1}^{n}\frac{A_{1m}^{(i)}}{(\mu_k-\alpha_i)}+\sum_{i=1}^{N-r}\frac{A_{2m}^{(i)}}{(\mu_k-\alpha_i)^2}+\right.$$
$$\left.+\sum_{i=1}^{n-r-t}\frac{A_{3m}^{(i)}}{(\mu_k-\alpha_i)^3}+\ldots\right\}\dot{I}_{\nu}^{(k-m)}=0 \tag{2.5}$$
$$(k=-\infty,\,\ldots,\,-1,\,0,\,1\,\ldots,\,\infty),$$

† Here and below we are assuming that $F_{1\mathrm{in}}/F_{2\mathrm{in}}\to\infty$ for $\mathrm{Re}(\lambda)\to\infty$.

where n is the number of different roots of the polynomial $F_{1in}(\mu_k)$, r being the number of simple roots, t the number of double roots etc.

Let us write the determinant of the system (2.5), viz.

$$\left|\begin{array}{l} \cdots\cdots\cdots\cdots\cdots\cdots\cdots\cdots\cdots \\ \ldots;\ 1+\sum_{i=1}^{n}\frac{A_{1,0}^{(i)}}{\mu_{-1}-\alpha_i}+\ldots;\sum_{i=1}^{n}\frac{A_{1,1}^{(i)}}{\mu_{-1}-\alpha_i}+\ldots;\ldots \\ \ldots;\quad \sum_{i=1}^{n}\frac{A_{1,-1}^{(i)}}{\mu_0-\alpha_i}+\ldots;\ 1+\sum_{i=1}^{n}\frac{A_{1,0}^{(i)}}{\mu_0-\alpha_i}+\ldots; \\ \qquad\qquad\qquad\qquad \sum_{i=1}^{n}\frac{A_{1,1}^{(i)}}{\mu_0-\alpha_i}+\ldots; \\ \ldots;\sum_{i=1}^{n}\frac{A_{1,-1}^{(i)}}{\mu_0-\alpha_i}+\ldots;\ 1+\sum_{i=1}^{n}\frac{A_{1,1}^{(i)}}{\mu_1-\alpha_i}+\ldots; \\ \cdots\cdots\cdots\cdots\cdots\cdots\cdots\cdots\cdots \end{array}\right| \tag{2.6}$$

By substituting $\mu_k=\lambda+jk\Omega$ we transform determinant (2.6). Without rewriting the determinant (2.6) anew, we shall restrict ourselves to writing down in their general form its diagonal and non-diagonal elements.

In this connexion we shall assume, to begin with, in order to simplify the argument and without detracting from generality, that all poles are simple or double.

A diagonal term of this determinant will have the form

$$1+\sum_{i=1}^{n}\frac{A_{10}^{(i)}}{\lambda+jk\Omega-\alpha_i}+\sum_{i=1}^{n-r}\frac{A_{20}^{(i)}}{(\lambda+jk\Omega-\alpha_i)^2}+\ldots; \tag{2.7}$$

and a non-diagonal term will be correspondingly equal to

$$\sum_{i=1}^{n}\frac{A_{1m}^{(i)}}{(\lambda+jk\Omega-\alpha_i)}+\sum_{i=1}^{n-r}\frac{A_{2m}^{(i)}}{(\lambda+jk\Omega-\alpha_i)^2}+\ldots. \tag{2.8}$$

Thus the difference in the determinant obtained from the corresponding determinant for Hill's equation is determined by the number of poles, by their order of multiplicity, which can be here, in the general case, of any order, and by the presence of a component α in the denominators of the elements of the determinant.

The determinant $\Delta(\lambda+jk\Omega)$ is a meromorphic function with poles at the points $(\alpha_1-jk\Omega)$, $(\alpha_2-jk\Omega)$, . . . , $(\alpha_n-jk\Omega)$. By expanding this determinant in a Laurent series in the neighbourhood of the points $\alpha_i-jk\Omega$, we obtain

$$\Delta(\lambda) = \Delta_1(\lambda)+\Delta_2(\lambda) = \Delta_1(\lambda)+ + \sum_{i=0}^{n} \Delta_{2i}^{(1)} + \sum_{i=0}^{n-r} \Delta_{2i}^{(2)}, \tag{2.9}$$

where $\Delta_1(\lambda)$ is the integral part, $\Delta_2(\lambda)$ is the fractional part of the expansion in a Laurent series and $\Delta_{2i}(\lambda)$ is equal to

$$\Delta_{2i}^{(1)}(\lambda) = \sum_{k=-\infty}^{\infty} C_{ik}^{(1)} (\lambda-\alpha_i+jk\Omega)^{-1} \quad (i = 1, 2, \ldots, n)$$

in the case of a simple pole and

$$\Delta_{2,i}^{(2)}(\lambda) = \sum_{k=-\infty}^{\infty} C_{ik}^{(2)} (\lambda-\alpha_i+jk\Omega)^{-2} \quad [i = 1, 2, \ldots n-r]. \tag{2.10}$$

in the case of a double pole.

The coefficient C_{ik} (in the case of a single pole) is equal to

$$C_{ik}^{(1)} = \lim_{\lambda\to(\alpha_i-jk\Omega)} [\Delta(\lambda)(\lambda-\alpha_i+jk\Omega)] \tag{2.11}$$

and respectively for a multiple pole of order two

$$C_{ik}^{(2)} = \lim_{\lambda\to(\alpha_i-jk\Omega)} [\Delta(\lambda)(\lambda-\alpha_i+jk\Omega)^2]. \tag{2.12}$$

The coefficients $C_{ik}^{(2)}$ generated by a pole of multiplicity r, where $r>l$, can be found according to the well-known rule. We have, for example, for the coefficient $C_{ik}^{(2)}$

$$C_{ik}^{(2)} = \left\{\frac{d}{d\lambda}[\Delta(\lambda)(\lambda-\alpha_i+jk\Omega)^2]\right\}_{\lambda=\alpha_{i-jk\Omega}}$$

We note that for all values of k $C_{ik}=D_i$ where D_i is a determinant analogous to Hill's determinant, equal for the case of a single pole to $D_i^{(1)}$. The elements of the central row of the determinant $D_i^{(1)}$ and of the row displaced by k rows downwards from the central row will have respectively the form

$$\ldots;\frac{A_{1,1}}{1};\frac{A_{1,0}}{1};\frac{A_{1,-1}}{1};\ldots$$

$$\ldots;\sum_{\xi=1}\frac{A_{i,1}}{\alpha_i-\alpha_\xi+jk\Omega};\ 1+\sum_{\xi=1}^{n}\frac{A_{i,0}}{\alpha_i-\alpha_\xi+jk\Omega};$$

$$\sum_{\xi=1}^{n}\frac{A_{i,-1}}{\alpha_i-\alpha_\xi+jk\,\Omega};\ \ldots \tag{2.13}$$

(for a double pole, the denominators of the elements of the determinant must be raised to the second power etc.).

Infinite numerical determinants, on the condition, which we have assumed, that $\sum_{m=-\infty}^{\infty}|L_{\nu\nu}^{(m)}|$ is a finite number (see (1.36)), are finite quantities. Then corresponding calculations can be easily carried out, if by taking the diagonal elements outside the sign of determinant D_i, we represent it as the product of a normal determinant times an infinite numerical series. It is easily verified that the terms of this series decrease not more slowly than s/k^2.

Below we shall assume $L_{\nu\nu}^{(m)}=\mu L_{\nu\nu}^{(m-1)}$. Thus the evaluation of the infinite numerical determinant D_i can be replaced, to an accuracy equal to ε, where ε is a small quantity assigned, by the evaluation of a finite determinant of rank not higher than $\varrho=\frac{1}{2}(1+2\,\nu/\varepsilon)$ obtained from the infinite determinant by bordering the central term.

The sum of all components of the main part of the Laurent series of the function $\Delta(\lambda+j\Omega)$ corresponding to a given value of the index is equal, for a double pole, to

$$\sum_{i=1}^{n-r}\Delta_{2,i}^{(2)}(\lambda)=\sum_{i=1}^{n-r}-\frac{D_i^{(2)}\pi^2}{\Omega^2\sin^2\left[(\lambda-\alpha_i)\pi\dfrac{1}{j\Omega}\right]}. \tag{2.14}$$

Correspondingly the component of the sum of the main parts of the functions $\Delta_{2i}^{(1)}(\lambda)$ for values of the index i will be equal, in the case of a simple pole, to†

$$\sum_{i=1}^{n-r} \Delta_{2,i}^{(1)}(\lambda) = \sum_{i=1}^{n-r} \cot\left[\pi(\lambda-\alpha_i)\frac{1}{j\Omega}\right]\frac{D_i^{(1)}\pi}{j\Omega}. \qquad (2.15)$$

By using the expressions (2.14) and (2.15) we can obtain the characteristic equation in a finite form.

According to (2.6)–(2.9) we can write

$$\Delta(\lambda) = \Delta_1(\lambda)+\Delta_2(\lambda) = \sum_{i=1}^{n}\Delta_{1,i}(\lambda)+ + \sum_{i=1}^{n}\Delta_{2,i}^{(1)}(\lambda)+\sum_{i=1}^{n-r}\Delta_{2,i}(\lambda). \qquad (2.16)$$

If Re $\lambda \to \infty$, it can be seen from (2.14) and (2.15) that $\Delta_2(\lambda)$ is a finite quantity.

The determinant $\Delta(\lambda)$ is also finite, since now all diagonal terms $\Delta_{ii} \to 1$ while the non-diagonal terms $\Delta_{ik} \to 0$. Accordingly, on the basis of Liouville's theorem, the integral part of $\Delta(\lambda)$, that is the value of $\Delta_2(\lambda)$, has a finite value equal to unity. By letting Re$\lambda \to \infty$, we obtain

$$\sum_{i=1}^{n}\Delta_{1i}(\lambda) = 1.$$

In the particular case when there is one double pole we obtain from (2.14) and (2.15)

$$\sin^2\left[\pi(\lambda-\alpha_1)\frac{1}{j\Omega}\right] = \pi^2 D_1^{(2)} 1/\Omega^2. \qquad (2.17)$$

In the case of b variable parameters, in the determinant $\Delta(\lambda)$, there are b rows with the same value k. That is, if in this case the lowest order of multiplicity of the root of the equation $F_2(\lambda)=0$ is equal to q, then the lowest order of the pole of the function $\Delta(\lambda)$ will be equal to $(q+b)$.

† In the presence in the equation $\Delta(p) = 0$ of a root of order three or higher, various combinations of trigonometrical functions occur, since terms of the type $\frac{\partial m}{\partial p^m}$ cot p will now occur. In particular (d/dp) $\cot p = -\operatorname{cosec}^2 p$.

CHAPTER III

OPERATIONAL ADMITTANCES AND SYSTEM FUNCTIONS OF CIRCUITS WITH VARIABLE PARAMETERS

In electrical engineering, radio engineering and control theory, the properties of electrical and dynamic circuits with constant parameters are described by means of system functions that characterize mathematically the corresponding circuit.

For example, to describe the properties of two-terminal networks, use is made of functions of the network input impedance or admittance, which connect the disturbance applied to the network with its response. To describe the transmission properties of a four-terminal network the transfer coefficient is used connecting the disturbance applied to its input with the response at the output of the network.

The behaviour of the transients occurring in the circuit is described by means of the frequency characteristic, corresponding to the system function, which is uniquely related to the transient response.

The frequency characteristic can be found both experimentally and analytically. The experimental determination of the frequency characteristic is carried out by applying to the circuit a sinusoidal disturbance and determining the circuit response for various values of the frequency of the applied disturbance. Analytically, the frequency characteristic can be determined from the equations describing the behaviour of the circuit when this is fed by a sinusoidal e.m.f., by successively eliminating from the equations all variables except the ones describing the behaviour of the circuit with respect to its terminals, and by evaluating the response for various values of ω_0.

We can pass from the equations for the response to a sinusoidal disturbance to the operational equations and vice versa, for zero initial conditions, by formally replacing $j\omega_0$ by p.

The system functions of linear circuits with constant parameters are uniquely determined by the physical parameters of the system.

In contrast to systems with constant parameters, for linear systems with variable parameters one cannot obtain directly a system function independent of the form of the perturbation and defined in terms of parameters of the system only. In other respects the theoretical and experimental determination of the spectra of the response of the system to various disturbances can be carried out for linear circuits with variable parameters in a similar manner as is done for circuits with constant parameters.

We shall consider in greater detail the definition of the concept of frequency characteristic of a circuit with periodically varying parameters.

The results obtained can be extended, as will be shown below, to systems with parameters varying according to an arbitrary law.

We shall consider now the derivation of an expression for the frequency characteristic of the input current of a two-pole network containing a single periodically-varying parameter.†

1. Circuit with a single periodically varying parameter

We shall consider an N-circuit network with one periodically varying parameter. Let us assume that in the ν-th circuit of this network there is an inductance, varying periodically with the fundamental frequency Ω. We shall find the frequency characteristic of the input current at the ν-th pair of terminals

† Below, without loss of generality, we shall use electrical engineernig terminology.

of this network. In order to find this characteristic we shall apply to the terminals of the ν-th circuit the e.m.f.[5]

$$\sum_{k=-\infty}^{\infty} U_m \cos(\omega_0 + k\Omega) = \text{Re} \sum_{k=-\infty}^{\infty} U_m e^{j(\omega_0 + k\Omega)t}, \qquad (3.1)$$

where ω_0 is the frequency of the disturbance applied and Ω is the frequency of variation of the parameter.

In this connexion, as is usual in electrical circuit theory and in control theory, we define the amplitude-phase frequency characteristic as the locus of the vectors of the system response to an applied sinusoidal disturbance the frequency of which varies from $\omega_0 = 0$ to $\omega_0 = \infty$. Here, however, in contrast to a system with constant parameters, the application of a sinusoidal disturbance of frequency ω_0 gives rise to a response containing an infinite number of harmonics with frequencies $\omega_0 + k\Omega$ where $k = -\infty, \ldots, -1, 0, +1, \ldots, \infty$.

In this case the values of the frequency characteristic corresponding to the frequencies $\omega_0 + k\Omega$ cannot be obtained independently of each other but are obtained simultaneously by applying a disturbance containing the entire frequency spectrum $\omega_0 + k\Omega$, as is taken into account in (3.1). The points of the frequency characteristic can be obtained sufficiently close to each other, separated by an interval $\Delta\omega_0$ chosen at will, except for the restriction that $\Delta\omega_0$ must satisfy the condition $\Omega/\Delta\omega_0 = n$, an integer.

According to what has been said, the system of equations, by means of which the frequency characteristic of a two-terminal network is determined, can be written down in the following manner

$$p[L_{\nu\nu}(t) \cdot i_{\nu\nu}(t)] + \sum_{s=1}^{N} M_{\nu s}(p) i_s(t) = $$
$$= \text{Re} \sum_{k=-\infty}^{\infty} \dot{U}_m e^{j(\omega_0 + k\Omega)t}; \qquad (3.2a)$$

$$\sum_{s=1}^{N} M_{\xi s}(p) i_s(t) = u(t) = 0$$
$$(\omega_0 = 0,\ \Delta\omega_0,\ 2\Delta\omega_0, \ldots,\ s\Delta\omega_0, \ldots, \infty), \qquad (3.2b)$$
$$(\xi = 1,\ 2, \ldots,\ \nu-1,\ \nu+1, \ldots, N),$$

where $M_{\xi s}(p)$ is a function of the operator $p = d/dt$ of the form

$$M_{s\nu}(p) = L_{s\nu}p + R_{s\nu} + \frac{1}{C_{s\nu}p},$$

and

$$L_{\nu\nu}(t) = 2l_{\nu\nu}^{(0)} + 2L_{\nu\nu}^{(1)} \cos(\Omega t + \alpha_1) + \dots + 2L_{\nu\nu}^{(m)} \cos(m\Omega t + \alpha_m) + \\ + \dots = \mathrm{Re} \sum_{m=-\infty}^{\infty} L_{\nu\nu}^{(m)} e^{jm\Omega t}, \text{ where } L_{\nu\nu}^{(0)} = 2l_{\nu\nu}^{(0)}.$$

In addition, the following notation has been used: ν is the index of the circuit in which the variable parameter is found and ξ are indices of circuits not containing variable parameters.

On the basis of the system of equations (3.1) and using the methods described in Chapter I, we obtain the following infinite system of equations for the determination of the frequency characteristic of the input current $I_\nu(j\omega_0)$ [Chapter II (2.1)]:

$$\left(L_{\nu\nu}^{(0)} + \frac{Z_{\text{in}}(j\omega_0 + jk\Omega)}{j\omega_0 + jk\Omega}\right)\dot{I}_\nu^{(k)} + \sum_{\substack{m=-\infty \\ m\neq 0}}^{\infty} L_{\nu\nu}^{(m)} \dot{I}_\nu^{(k-m)} = \\ = \frac{\dot{U}_m e^{j(\omega_0 + k\Omega)t}}{j(\omega_0 + k\Omega)} \\ (k = -\infty, \dots, -1, 0, 1, \dots, \infty). \tag{3.3}$$

Proceeding from the system of equations (3.3) we can pass, for zero initial conditions, to a system of operational equations; in this connexion we obtain

$$\left(L_{\nu\nu}^{(0)} + \frac{Z_{\nu\text{in}}(p + jk\Omega)}{p + jk\Omega}\right)\dot{I}_\nu(p + jk\Omega) + \sum_{\substack{m=-\infty \\ m\neq 0}}^{\infty} L_{\nu\nu}^{(m)} \dot{I}_\nu[p - j(m-k)\Omega] = \\ = \frac{\dot{U}_m(p + jk\Omega)}{p + jk\Omega} \\ (k = -\infty, \dots, -1, 0, 1, \dots, \infty). \tag{3.4}$$

By determining from (3.4) the transform of the response of the system $I_\nu(p)$, we see that here, in contrast to a network with constant parameters, instead of a relation of the type $I(p)=U(p)/Z(p)$ a more complicated relation occurs, $I(p)=F[U(p);\, Z(p)]$, where F is a function expressing the dependence of the system response to the disturbance applied upon the system parameters; i.e. in this case these parameters cannot be isolated as is the case for systems with constant parameters.

On the basis of the system of equations (3.4) an expression can be found determining $I_\nu(j\omega)$, i.e. the frequency characteristic of the input current of the ν-th circuit and the operational admittance $I_\nu(p)$.

However, for the sake of completeness of our exposition and greater rigour, we shall determine the transform of the current i_ν, i.e. $L[i_\nu(t)]=I_\nu(p)$ (and subsequently shall pass formally to the frequency characteristic) by proceeding directly from the equations (3.2) to their transforms.

If we take the transforms of both sides of (3.2) and take into account that in this case the applied voltage is $U(t)$, we obtain, after substituting $L_{\nu\nu}(t)$ on the basis of the displacement theorem,

$$p\left[L_{\nu\nu}^{(0)} I_\nu(p) + \sum_{\substack{m=-\infty \\ m\neq 0}}^{\infty} L_{\nu\nu}^{(m)} I_\nu(p-jm\,\Omega)e^{-j\alpha_m}\right] +$$

$$+\sum_{s=1}^{N} M_{\nu s}(p) I_s(p) = U(p);$$

$$\sum_{s=1}^{N} M_{\xi s}(p) I_s(p) = 0$$

$$(\xi = 1,\ 2,\ \ldots,\ \nu-1,\ \nu+1,\ \ldots,\ N). \tag{3.5}$$

Assuming that no applied voltages are present in any circuit of the network except the ν-th circuit, we express in (3.2b) all currents $I_\xi(p)$ for $\xi \neq \nu$ in terms of the current I_ν; we obtain

$$I_\xi(p) = Z_{\xi\nu}(p) I_\nu(p), \text{ where } Z_{\xi\nu} = \frac{\Delta_\xi}{\Delta}\,. \tag{3.6}$$

Substituting the currents $I_\xi(p)$ from (3.6) in (3.2), we obtain

$$p\left[L_{\nu\nu}^{(0)}I_\nu(p)+\sum_{\substack{m=-\infty\\ m\neq 0}}^{\infty} L_{\nu\nu}^{(m)}I_\nu(p-jm\,\Omega)e^{-ja_m}\right]+$$

$$+\sum_{s=1}^{N} Z_{\nu\mathrm{in}}\,(p)I_\nu(p) = U(p), \tag{3.7}$$

where

$$Z_{\nu\mathrm{in}}(p) = \sum_{s=1}^{N} M_{\nu\nu}(p)+M_{\nu s}(p)Z_{s\nu}(p)].$$

Equation (3.7) contains an infinite number of unknowns $I(p)$, $I(p-j\Omega)$, $I(p+j\Omega)$, $\ldots$, $I(p-mj\Omega)$, $I(p+mj\Omega)$ etc. On replacing p in the system (3.7) by $(p+j\Omega)$, $(p-j\Omega)$, $\ldots$, $(p+jm\Omega)$, $(p-jm\Omega)$, $\ldots$ etc, we obtain an infinite system of equations with an infinite number of unknowns.

This system of equations has the following form

$$(p+jk\,\Omega)\left\{L_{\nu\nu}^{(0)}I_\nu(p+jk\Omega)+\right.$$

$$\left.+\sum_{m=-\infty}^{\infty} L_{\nu\nu}^{(m)}I_\nu[p-j(m-k)\,\Omega]e^{-ja_{m-k}}\right\}+$$

$$+Z_{\nu\mathrm{in}}\,(p+jk\,\Omega)I_\nu(p+jk\,\Omega) = U(p+jk\,\Omega);$$

$$(k = -\infty,\ \ldots,\ -1,\ 0,\ 1,\ \ldots,\ \infty). \tag{3.8}$$

Let us introduce the notation

$$\frac{Z_{\nu\mathrm{in}}\,(p+jk\,\Omega)}{p+jk\,\Omega} = \frac{F_{1\mathrm{in}}\,(p+jk\,\Omega)}{F_{2\mathrm{in}}(p+jk\,\Omega)} \tag{3.9}$$

and let us impose the condition that for

$$\mathrm{Re}\,p\to\infty,\ \frac{F_{1\mathrm{in}}\,(p+jk\,\Omega)}{F_{2\mathrm{in}}\,(p+jk\,\Omega)}\to\infty.$$

By substituting (3.9) in (3.8), we obtain after simple transformations

$$\left[1+\frac{L_{vv}^{(0)}F_{2\text{in}}(p+jk\Omega)}{F_{1\text{in}}(p+jk\Omega)}\right]I_v(p+jk\Omega)+$$

$$+\frac{F_{2\text{in}}(p+jk\Omega)}{F_{1\text{in}}(p+jk\Omega)}\sum_{\substack{m=-\infty\\ m\neq 0}}^{\infty}L_{vv}^{(m)}I_v[p+j(m-k)\Omega]=$$

$$=\frac{U(p+jk\Omega)}{p+jk\Omega}\,\frac{F_{2\text{in}}(p+jk\Omega)}{F_{1\text{in}}(p+jk\Omega)}. \tag{3.10}$$

Let us introduce the notation

$$(p+jk\Omega)=\mu_k;$$

$$\frac{U(p+jk\Omega)}{p+jk\Omega}\cdot\frac{F_2(p+jk\Omega)}{F_1(p+jk\Omega)}=\Phi(p+jk\Omega) \tag{3.11}$$

and, assuming all roots of the polynomial

$$\alpha_1,\ \alpha_2,\ \ldots,\ \alpha_n$$

to be simple, let us rewrite the equation (3.10) in the following manner

$$\left[1+\sum_{i=1}^{N}\frac{A_{10}^{(i)}}{\mu_k-\alpha_i}\right]I_v(p+jk\Omega)+$$

$$+\sum_{\substack{m=-\infty\\ m\neq 0}}^{\infty}\sum_{i=1}^{n}\frac{A^{(i)}}{\mu_k-\alpha_i}I_v[p+j(m-k)\Omega]=\Phi(p+jk\Omega). \tag{3.12}$$

According to Chapter II the determinant of the system (3.11) is equal to

$$\Delta(p)=1-\sum_{i=1}^{n}\cot\left[\pi(p-\alpha_i)\frac{1}{j\Omega}\right]\frac{\pi D_i^{(1)}}{j\Omega}, \tag{3.13}$$

where $D_i^{(1)}$ is a determinant, analogous to Hill's determinant, equal to

$$\left|\begin{array}{l} \cdots\cdots\cdots\cdots\cdots\cdots\cdots\cdots\cdots\cdots \\ 1+\sum\limits_{\substack{i=1\\ \xi\neq i}}^{n}\dfrac{A_{1,0}^{(i)}}{j\Omega+\alpha_\xi-\alpha_i}\,;\ \sum\limits_{\substack{i=1\\ \xi\neq i}}^{n}\dfrac{A_{1,-1}^{(i)}}{j\Omega+\alpha_\xi-\alpha_i}\,;\ \ldots \\ \qquad\qquad \ldots;\dfrac{A_{1,1}}{1}\,;\ \dfrac{A_{1,0}}{1}\,;\ \dfrac{A_{1,-1}}{1}\,;\ \ldots \\ \ldots;\sum\limits_{\substack{i=1\\ \xi\neq i}}^{n}\dfrac{A_{1,1}^{(i)}}{-j\Omega+\alpha_\xi-\alpha_i}\,;\ 1+\sum\limits_{\substack{i=1\\ \xi\neq i}}^{n}\dfrac{A_{1,0}^{(i)}}{-j\Omega+\alpha_\xi-\alpha_i}\,;\ \ldots \\ \cdots\cdots\cdots\cdots\cdots\cdots\cdots\cdots\cdots\cdots \end{array}\right| \tag{3.14}$$

We find for the current, from the system (3.12)

$$I(p) = \frac{\Delta_1(p)}{\Delta(p)}\,. \tag{3.15}$$

Reduction of the determinant $\Delta_1(p)$ to a finite form.

Let us in the first place discuss the case of a system having a single periodically varying parameter.

In this case the determinant $\Delta_1(p)$ will have the form

$$\Delta_1(p) = \left|\begin{array}{l} \ldots;\ a_{1,2};\ a_{1,1};\ \Phi(p+j\Omega);\ a_{1,1};\ a_{1,-2};\ \ldots \\ \ldots;\ a_{0,2};\ a_{0,1};\ \Phi(p);\ a_{0,1};\ a_{0,-2};\ \ldots \\ \ldots;\ a_{-1,3};\ a_{-1,2};\ \Phi(p-j\Omega);\ a_{-1,1};\ a_{-1,-2};\ldots \end{array}\right| \tag{3.16}$$

On expanding the determinant $\Delta_1(p)$ with respect to minors, we shall obtain

$$\Delta_1 = \Phi(p)\Delta_{00}+\Phi(p+j\Omega)\Delta_{1,0}+\Phi(p-j\Omega)\Delta_{-1,0}+\ \ldots\ + \\ +\Phi(p+js\Omega)\Delta_{s0}+\ \ldots \tag{3.17}$$

Let us consider, for example, the determinant $\Delta_{s0}(p)$. We obtain this determinant from the determinant $\Delta_1(p)$ by cancelling the s-th row and the zero-th column.

On expanding this determinant in a Laurent series, we shall write

$$\Delta_{s0} = \Delta_{1s0}(p)+\Delta_{2s0}(p), \tag{3.18}$$

where $\Delta_{1s0}(p)$ is the integral part and $\Delta_{2s0}(p)$ is the fractional part of the Laurent series

By taking into account that the s-th row is absent, the fractional part of the Laurent series will be written in the form

$$\Delta_{2s0} = \sum_{i=1}^{n} \Delta_{2s0i} = \sum_{i=1}^{n} \sum_{\substack{k=-\infty \\ k\neq s}}^{\infty} C_{iks}^{(1)}(p-\alpha_i+jk\Omega)^{-1} \qquad (3.19)$$

where

$$C_{iks}^{(1)} = lim\ [\Delta_{s0}\,(p-\alpha_i+jk\Omega)]$$
$$p \to (\alpha_j - jk\Omega).$$

Let us examine the properties of the numerical determinant

$$C_{iks}^{(1)}$$

In contrast to above, the $C_{iks}^{(1)}$ are not equal to each other for different values, since the s-th row is absent in the determinant Δ_{s0}. For a given value of k, the row of the determinant $\Delta_{s0}(p)$, in which the quantity $k\Omega$ occurs and which corresponds to the k-th row of the determinant $\Delta_{s0}(p)$, becomes the central row of the infinite numerical determinant $C_{iks}^{(1)}$. That is the central row of the determinant $C_{iks}^{(1)}$ will be distant from the missing row by $\nu = s-k$ rows.

Under the conditions assumed (see (1.36)), the evaluation of the infinite determinant $D_i^{(1)}$ can be replaced, to an accuracy ε, by the evaluation of a finite determinant obtained by bordering the central term of $D_i^{(1)}$.The rank of the finite determinant being evaluated will be not higher than $2\varrho+1$, where $\varrho > (1+2\nu/\varepsilon)2$. If $|\,s-k\,| > \varrho$, then, owing to a property of the determinant $D_i^{(1)}$, we can assume to an accuracy ε that the determinant $C_{iks}^{(1)}$ does not depend on k, i.e. $C_{iks}^{(1)} = C_{is}^{(1)}$ and is equal, to an accuracy ε, to $D_{i0}^{(1)}$ (since, as has been shown, the value of an infinite numerical determinant is found to an accuracy ε and under the conditions mentioned, by evaluating a finite numerical determinant obtained by bordering the central term). We obtain the determinant $D_{i0}^{(1)}$ from $D_i^{(1)}$ by cancelling the zero-th column and all rows that are distant from the central one by more than ϱ rows.

If, however, condition $(k-s)>\varrho$ is not satisfied, then we shall have for this interval $2\varrho+1$ different values of $C_{iks}^{(1)}$ corresponding to the values $\nu = k-s = -\varrho, \ldots, 1, 0, 1, \ldots \infty$. We shall obtain the determinants $C_{iks}^{(1)}$ from the determinant by cancelling the 0-th columns and the ν-th row.

Thus the value of C_{iks} depends on ν only; for example $C_{ilm} = C_{irt}$ if $l-m = r-t$, where l, r, m and t are values of k and s.

Let us, by taking what has been expounded into account, transform (3.19).

By splitting in (3.19) the sum with respect to k into two parts, we shall separate the values of $C_{iks}^{(1)}$ corresponding to values of $(k-s)<\varrho$ and shall take into account that the remaining $C_{iks} = C_{is}$, do not, to an accuracy ε, depend on k. We shall obtain as a result

$$\Delta_{2s0} = \sum_{i=1}^{n} \left\{ \sum_{\substack{k=-\infty \\ k\neq s}}^{s-\varrho+1} C_{is}^{(1)} (p-\alpha_i+jk\Omega)^{-1} + \sum_{k=s+(\varrho+1)}^{\infty} C_{is}^{(1)} (p-\alpha_i+jk\Omega)^{-1} + \sum_{\substack{k=s-\varrho \\ k\neq s}}^{s+\varrho} C_{iks}^{(1)} (p-\alpha_i+jk\Omega)^{-1} \right\} \tag{3.20}$$

The expression (3.20) can be rewritten in the following manner:

$$\Delta_{2s0} = \sum_{i=1}^{n} \left\{ \sum_{\substack{k=-\infty \\ k\neq s}}^{s-(\varrho+1)} C_{is}^{(1)} (p-\alpha_i+jk\Omega)^{-1} + \sum_{\substack{k=s+(\varrho+1) \\ k\neq s}}^{\infty} C_{is}^{(1)} (p-\alpha_i+jk\Omega)^{-1} + \right.$$
$$- \sum_{\substack{k=s-\varrho \\ k\neq s}}^{s+\varrho} C_{is}^{(1)} (p-\alpha_i+jk\Omega)^{-1} + \sum_{\substack{k=s-\varrho \\ k\neq s}}^{s+\varrho} C_{is}^{(1)} (p-\alpha_i+jk\Omega)^{-1} +$$
$$\left. + \sum_{\substack{k=s-\varrho \\ k\neq s}}^{s+\varrho} C_{iks}^{(1)} (p-\alpha_i+jk\Omega)^{-1} \right\} \tag{3.21}$$

By taking into account that, according to what has been expounded above, all $C_{is}^{(1)}$ are, to the accuracy assumed, equal to each other, by combining the first three sums, by taking $C_{is}^{(1)} = D_{is}^{(1)}$ outside the sign of sum, and by replacing the sum with infinite limits, obtained, by the cotangent, we shall obtain (for the case of a simple pole).

$$\Delta_{2s0} = \sum_{i=1}^{n} \left\{ D_{i0}^{(1)} \frac{\pi}{j\Omega} \cot (p-\alpha_i) \frac{\pi}{j\Omega} + \sum_{\substack{k=s-\varrho \\ k \neq s}}^{s+\varrho} C_{iks}^{(1)} (p-\alpha_i+jk\Omega)^{-1} + \right.$$

$$\left. + \sum_{\substack{k=s-\varrho \\ k \neq s}}^{s+\varrho} D_{i0}^{(1)} (p-\alpha_i+jk\Omega)^{-1} \right\} \tag{3.22}$$

Correspondingly by taking into account that $k = s+\nu$, we shall have

$$\sum_{s=-\infty}^{\infty} \Phi(p+js\Omega)\Delta_{s0} = \sum_{s=-\infty}^{\infty} \Phi(p+js\Omega) (\Delta_{1s0}+\Delta_{2s0}) =$$

$$= \sum_{s=-\infty}^{\infty} \Phi(p+js\Omega) + \sum_{s=-\infty}^{\infty} \Phi(p+js\Omega) \sum_{i=1}^{n} \left\{ D_{i0}^{(1)} \frac{\pi}{j\Omega} \cot (p-\alpha_i) \frac{\pi}{j\Omega} + \right.$$

$$\left. + \sum_{\nu=-\varrho}^{\varrho} C_{i\nu}^{(1)} (p-\alpha_i+j(s+\nu)\Omega]^{-1} + \sum_{\nu=-\varrho}^{\varrho} D_{i0}^{(1)} [p-\alpha_i j(s+\nu)\Omega]^{-1} \right\} \tag{3.23}$$

In the particular case $u(t) = \delta(t)$, we shall have for $\Phi(p) = U(p)/p$

$$\sum_{s=-\infty}^{\infty} \Phi(p+js\Omega) = \sum_{s=-\infty}^{\infty} \frac{1}{p+js\Omega} = \frac{\pi}{j\Omega} \cot \frac{\pi\varrho}{j\Omega} \tag{3.24}$$

By taking (3.24) [(3.18)–(3.22)] into account, we shall rewrite (3.23) in the following manner

$$\Delta_1(p) \cong \frac{\pi}{j\Omega} \cot \frac{\pi\varrho}{j\Omega} \left[1 + \sum_{i=1}^{n} \frac{\pi D_{i0}}{j\Omega} \cot (p-\alpha_i) \frac{\pi}{j\Omega} \right] +$$

$$+ \sum_{s=-\infty}^{\infty} \sum_{\nu=-\varrho}^{\varrho} A_{i\nu}^{(1)} \sum_{i=1}^{n} \left[\frac{(\alpha_i+j\nu\Omega)^{-1}}{p+js\Omega} - \frac{(\alpha_i+j\nu\Omega)^{-1}}{p-\alpha_i+j(s-\nu)\Omega} \right] \tag{3.25}$$

Here we have introduced the notation $A_{i\nu}^{(1)} = C_{i\nu}^{(1)} - D_{i0}^{(1)}$ and have taken into account that $\Delta_{1s0} = 1$.

Thus we shall obtain, finally, for the case when $\Delta(p)$ has only simple poles,

$$\Delta_1(p) \cong \frac{\pi}{j\Omega} \cot \frac{\pi p}{j\Omega} \left\{ 1 + \sum_{i=1}^{n} D_{i0}^{(1)} \frac{\pi}{j\Omega} \cot (p-\alpha_i) \frac{\pi}{j\Omega} \right\} +$$

$$+ \sum_{i=1}^{n} \sum_{\nu=-\varrho}^{\varrho} \frac{A_{i\nu}^{(1)}}{p_i + j\nu\Omega} \left[\frac{\pi}{j\Omega} \cot \frac{\pi\varrho}{j\Omega} - \frac{\pi}{j\Omega} \cot (p - \alpha_i + j\nu\Omega) \frac{\pi}{j\Omega} \right] \quad (3.26)$$

Corresponding expressions can also be derived for the cases when there are multiple poles of $\Delta(p)$ while the disturbance applied is not represented by a δ-function but by a unit step or by a sinusoidal function.

The analysis can be carried out in a similar manner, also in the case when not one but b parameters vary periodically.

The difference will consist in that here, instead of infinite numerical determinants $D_i^{(r)}$ $(r = 1, 2, \ldots)$, determinants $D_i^{(r+b)}$ will occur.

The following theorem follows from what has been expounded.

THEOREM 1. The transform of the response, to an applied disturbance of the form $\delta(t)$, $1(t)$, or $e^{\alpha t}$, of a system containing parameters that vary according to the law $b(t) = \sum_{r=-\infty}^{\infty} b^{(r)} e^{jr\Omega t}$, where $\sum_{r=-\infty}^{\infty} b^{(r)}$ is finite and, beginning from a certain value of r, $a^{(r)} = \mu a(r-1)$ $(\omega = 1)$, can be represented, to any assigned accuracy, as a rational function of argument exp $(\pi p/j\Omega)$.

CHAPTER IV

CALCULATION OF TRANSIENTS BY THE FOURIER-SERIES METHOD

1. Theoretical principles

In the calculation of transients by the Fourier-series method the actual transient process, occurring when a sinusoidal-voltage source is applied to the circuit considered, is replaced [11] by several periodic processes which would occur if at

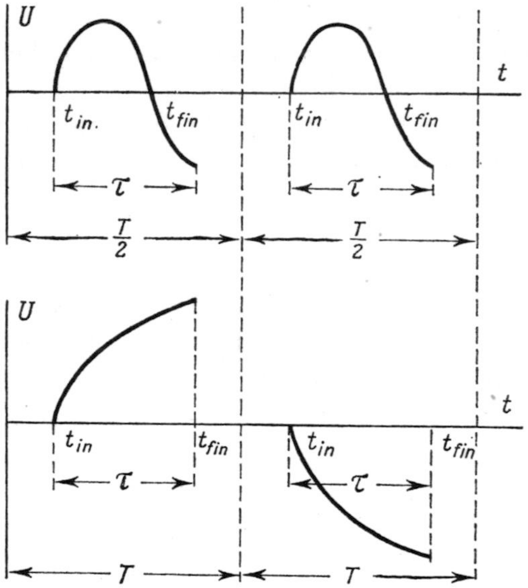

FIG. 2. To illustrate the Fourier-series method

equal intervals of time the source indicated were alternately connected to and disconnected from the circuit. In this case, if the voltage applied is sinusoidal, in the circuit there will act a voltage represented by a periodized segment of a sinusoid (Fig. 2).

If the voltage source is connected to the circuit at the initial instant of time t_{in}, is then disconnected after a time interval τ at the instant of time $t_{fin} = t_{in}+\tau$, and is again connected to the circuit at the instant of time $t = T/2+t_{in}$ with opposite polarity of the circuit terminals, the curve of the acting voltage will have the form shown in Fig. 2. Such a periodic voltage, acting for an interval τ, can be represented in the form of a Fourier series

$$u_\tau(t) = \text{Re} \sum_{s=1}^{\infty} \dot{U}_s e^{j(s\omega t+\Theta_{Us})}. \tag{4.1}$$

Here ω is the angular frequency of periodization (calculated quantity).

In an analogous manner the current $i_\tau(t)$, flowing in the circuit under the conditions considered of periodic connection and disconnection, will also be represented in the form of a Fourier series

$$i_\tau(t) = \text{Re} \sum_{s=1}^{\infty} \dot{I}_s e^{j(s\omega t+\varphi_s)}. \tag{4.1a}$$

Here the amplitudes $\dot{U}_s$ and $\dot{I}_s$ are determined by the relations

$$\dot{U}_s = \frac{2}{T}\int_0^{T/2} u_\tau(t)e^{-js\omega t}\,dt; \tag{4.2}$$

$$\dot{I}_s = \frac{2}{T}\int_0^{T/2} i_\tau(t)e^{-js\omega t}\,dt. \tag{4.3}$$

In this connection as a result of the manner of periodization chosen (a periodic variation of the sign of the voltage applied) the series for $u_\tau(t)$ and $i_\tau(t)$ will only contain terms with odd values of s.

Proceeding from the expressions for the complex amplitudes of the harmonics of current $\dot{I}_s$ and the expression for $\dot{U}_s$, expressions can be determined for the complex amplitudes of the potential drops across the inductance. For the complex amplitude of the potential drop across the inductance we obtain, after integrating by parts, the following expression

$$\dot{U}_{Ls} = \frac{2}{T}\int_0^{T/2} u_{L\tau}(t)e^{-js\omega t}\,dt = \frac{2L}{T}\int_0^{T/2}\frac{di_{L\tau}}{dt}e^{-js\omega t}dt =$$

$$= \left|\frac{2L}{T}i_{L\tau}(t)e^{-js\omega t}\right|_{t_{\text{in}}}^{t_{\text{fin}}} + \frac{js\omega L\cdot 2}{T}\int_0^{T/2} i_{L\tau}(t)e^{-js\omega t}\,dt =$$

$$= \frac{2L}{T}[i_{L\tau}(t_{\text{fin}})e^{-js\omega t_{\text{fin}}} - i_{L\tau}(t_{\text{in}})e^{-js\omega t_{\text{in}}}] +$$

$$+ js\omega L\dot{I}_s = U_{\delta Ls}t(_{\text{in}};\, t_{\text{fin}}) + js\omega L\dot{I}_s, \tag{4.4}$$

correspondingly we obtain for the complex amplitude of the current flowing through the capacitance

$$\dot{I}_{cs} = \frac{2C}{T}\int_0^{T/2}\frac{du_{c\tau}(t)}{dt}e^{-js\omega t}\,dt = js\omega C\dot{U}_{cs} + \dot{I}_{\delta cs}(t_{\text{in}};\, t_{\text{fin}})$$

or

$$\dot{U}_{cs} = \frac{\dot{I}_{cs}}{js\omega C} - \frac{\dot{I}_{\delta cs}(t_{\text{in}};\, t_{\text{fin}})}{js\omega C}. \tag{4.5}$$

In the expressions (4.4) and (4.5) there appears in the right-hand side an additional term in comparison with the usual expression for a steady-state mode of operation. It can be shown that this additional term represents the result of the expansion in a Fourier series of the impulse function (the δ-function) multiplied by a constant coefficient.[13]

Physically, this additional term is caused by the fact that in the periodic process considered, by which we have replaced the actual process, impulse voltage jumps appear across the inductances of the circuit at the instant of connection for $t = t_{in}$ and at the instant of disconnection for $t = t_{fin}$. In a similar manner impulse current jumps occur at these instants of time in the capacitances of the circuit.

The impulse voltages and currents form a periodic impulse function which is equal alternatively to plus or minus infinity at the points $t_{in} \pm nT/2$ and $t_{fin} \pm nT/2$ and is equal to zero at all remaining points. As is usual we shall denote by δ the derivative of a unit step and the expression for the periodized δ-function, repeating itself at the instants $t_{in} \pm nT/2$ with an alternate sign, will be written in the form $\delta(t_{in} \pm nT/2) \times (-1)^n$, where $n = 0, 1, 2$, etc.

Correspondingly the expression for a periodized impulse function, which at the instants $t_{in} \pm nT/2$ and $t_{fin} \pm nT/2$ is not the derivative of a unit step but the derivative of a step of magnitude $f(t_{in})$ or $f(t_{fin})$ can be written in the form

$$f_\delta(t) = \left[f(t_{in})\,\delta\left(t_{in} \pm n\frac{T}{2}\right) - \right.$$
$$\left. - f(t_{fin})\,\delta\left(t_{fin} \pm n\frac{T}{2}\right)\right](-1)^n. \tag{4.6}$$

If we determine for the expression (4.4) the Fourier-series coefficients $\dot{U}_{\delta s}(t_{in}, t_{fin})$ according to the formula

$$\dot{U}_{\delta s}(t_{in};\ t_{fin}) = \frac{2}{T}\int_0^{T/2} f_\delta(t)e^{-js\omega t}\,dt, \tag{4.7}$$

expressions will be obtained that have been denoted in (4.4) by $\dot{U}_{\delta Ls}(t_{in};\ t_{fin})$.

The method of calculation of a transient process by means of Fourier series can also be employed for the calculation of processes in circuits with periodically varying parameters.[11, 13]

We can also obtain in these systems expressions for the complex amplitudes of the harmonic components of the voltage drop across a periodically varying inductance or capacitance, similar to the expressions obtained above when considering the forced component.

In fact, for the voltage drop across an inductance varying periodically according to the relation

$$L(t) = L_0(1+m\cos\Omega t), \tag{4.8}$$

we obtain, by bearing in mind the expressions (4.4), (4.5) and (1.26) for $\omega = \Omega/n$ where n is an integer,

$$\frac{d}{dt}[L(t)\cdot i(t)] = \frac{d}{dt}\left\{\operatorname{Re}L_0\left[\sum_{k=-\infty}^{\infty}\sum_{s=1}^{\infty}\dot{I}_{s+kn}e^{j(s+kn)\omega t}+\right.\right.$$

$$\left.\left.+\frac{\overset{*}{m}}{2}\sum_{k=-\infty}^{\infty}\sum_{s=1}^{\infty}\dot{I}_{s+kn}e^{j[s+(k-1)n]\omega t}+\frac{\dot{m}}{2}\sum_{k=-\infty}^{\infty}\sum_{s=1}^{\infty}\dot{I}_{s+kn}e^{j[s+(k+1)n]\omega t}\right]\right\}=$$

$$=\operatorname{Re}L_0\left\{\sum_{k=-\infty}^{\infty}\sum_{s=1}^{\infty}j(s+kn)\omega\cdot\dot{I}_{s+kn}e^{j(s+kn)\omega t}+\right.$$

$$+\frac{\dot{m}}{2}\sum_{k=-\infty}^{\infty}\sum_{s=1}^{\infty}j[s+(k+1)n]\omega\dot{I}_{s+kn}e^{j[s+(k+1)n]\omega t}+$$

$$+\frac{\overset{*}{m}}{2}\sum_{k=-\infty}^{\infty}\sum_{s=1}^{\infty}j[s+(k-1)n]\omega\dot{I}_{s+kn}e^{j[s+(k-1)n]\omega t}+$$

$$+\frac{2}{T}\sum_{k=-\infty}^{\infty}\sum_{s=0}^{\infty}[i_\tau(t_{\text{fin}})e^{-j(s+kn)\omega t_{\text{fin}}}-i_\tau(t_{\text{in}})e^{-j(s+kn)\omega t_{\text{in}}}]+$$

$$+\frac{\dot{m}}{T}\sum_{k=-\infty}^{\infty}\sum_{s=1}^{\infty}[i_\tau(t_{\text{fin}})e^{-j[s+(k+1)n]\omega t_{\text{fin}}}-i_\tau(t_{\text{in}})e^{-j[s+(k+1)n]\omega t_{\text{in}}}]+$$

$$+\frac{\overset{*}{m}}{T}\sum_{k=-\infty}^{\infty}\sum_{s=1}^{\infty}[i_\tau(t_{\text{fin}})e^{-j[s+(k-1)n]\omega t_{\text{fin}}}-i_\tau(t_{\text{in}})e^{-j[s+(k-1)n]\omega t_{\text{in}}}. \tag{4.9}$$

We obtain finally for $t_{\text{in}} = 0$

$$\frac{d}{dt}[L(t)\cdot i(t)] = \operatorname{Re}L_0\left\{\sum_{k=-\infty}^{\infty}\sum_{s=1}^{\infty}j(s+kn)\omega\cdot\dot{I}_{s+kn}\cdot e^{j(s+kn)\omega t}+\right.$$

$$+\frac{\dot{m}}{2}\sum_{k=-\infty}^{\infty}\sum_{s=1}^{\infty}j[s+(k+1)n]\omega\cdot\dot{I}_{s+kn}\cdot e^{j[s+(k+1)n]\omega t}+$$

$$+\frac{\overset{*}{m}}{2}\sum_{k=-\infty}^{\infty}\sum_{s=1}^{\infty} j(s+(k-1)n)\omega\cdot \dot{I}_{s+kn}e^{j[s+(k-1)n]\omega t}+$$

$$+\frac{2}{T}\sum_{k=-\infty}^{\infty}\sum_{s=1}^{\infty}[i_\tau(t_{\text{fin}})e^{-j(s+kn)\omega t_{\text{fin}}}-i_\tau(0)]+$$

$$+\frac{\dot{m}}{T}\sum_{k=-\infty}^{\infty}\sum_{s=1}^{\infty}[i_\tau(t_{\text{fin}})e^{-j[s+(k+1)nt]\omega t}-i_\tau(0)]+$$

$$+\frac{\overset{*}{m}}{T}\sum_{k=-\infty}^{\infty}\sum_{s=1}^{\infty}[i_\tau(t_{\text{fin}})e^{-j[s+(k+1)n]\omega t}-i_\tau(0)]\Big\}. \tag{4.10}$$

The transients in the circuit of Fig. 1 are determined by the equation

$$\frac{d(Li)}{dt}+ri+u_c=\text{Re}\sum_{s=-\infty}^{\infty}U_s e^{js\omega t}. \tag{4.11}$$

After substituting (4.1), (4.1a), (4.5) and (4.9) in (4.11) we obtain

$$\frac{1}{2}\sum_{k=-\infty}^{\infty}\sum_{s=1}^{\infty}\Big\{\Big[j(s+kn)\omega L_0+r+\frac{1}{j(s+kn)\omega C}\Big]\dot{I}_{s+kn}e^{j(s+kn)\omega t}+$$

$$+\frac{\dot{m}L_0}{4}\sum_{k=-\infty}^{\infty}\sum_{s=1}^{\infty} j[s+(k+1)n]\omega\dot{I}_{s+kn}e^{j[s+(k+1)n]\omega t}+$$

$$+\frac{\overset{*}{m}L_0}{4}\sum_{k=-\infty}^{\infty}\sum_{s=1}^{\infty} j[s+(k-1)n]\omega\dot{I}_{s+kn}e^{j[s+(k-1)n]\omega t}=$$

$$=\frac{1}{2}\sum_{s=1}^{\infty}\dot{U}_s e^{js\omega t}-\frac{1}{T}\sum_{k=-\infty}^{\infty}[i(t_{\text{fin}})e^{-j(s+kn)t_{\text{fin}}}-$$

$$-i(t_{\text{in}})e^{-j[s+kn]t_{\text{in}}}]+\frac{1}{j\pi}\sum_{k=-\infty}^{\infty}\sum_{s=1}^{\infty}[u_\tau(t_{\text{fin}})e^{-j(s+kn)\omega t_{\text{fin}}}-$$

$$-u_\tau(t_{\text{fin}})e^{-j(s+kn)\omega t_{\text{fin}}}]-$$

$$-\frac{L_0\cdot\dot{m}}{2T}\sum_{k=-\infty}^{\infty}\sum_{s=1}^{\infty}[i_\tau(t_{\text{fin}})e^{-j[s+(k+1)n]\omega t_{\text{fin}}}-$$

$$-i_\tau(t_{\text{in}})e^{-j[s+(k+1)n]\omega t_{\text{in}}}]-\frac{L_0\overset{*}{m}}{2T}\sum_{k=-\infty}^{\infty}\sum_{s=1}^{\infty}[i_\tau(t_{\text{fin}})\times$$

$$\times e^{-j[s+(k-1)n]\omega t_{\text{fin}}}-i_\tau(t_{\text{in}})e^{-j[s+(k-1)n]\omega t_{\text{in}}}], \tag{4.12}$$

where $\dot{I}_{s+kn}$ is the complex amplitude of the harmonic component of frequency $(s+kn)\omega$.

On changing the indices in a similar manner as has been done in Chapter I in passing from (1.10) to (1.11) and by introducing for the amplitudes indices equal to the frequency of the oscillation to which this complex amplitude corresponds, we obtain for the oscillations of frequency $(s+kn)\omega$, by writing the expression in full,

. . . .

$$\frac{\dot{m}}{2} j\omega L_0 \dot{I}_{s-2n} + \left(j\omega L_0 + \frac{r}{s-n} + \frac{1}{j(s-n)^2\omega C}\right)\dot{I}_{s-n} + $$
$$+ \frac{\overset{*}{m}}{2} j\omega L_0 \dot{I}_s = \frac{\dot{U}_{s-n}}{s-n} + \frac{\dot{f}_{s-n}(t_{\text{in}};\ t_{\text{fin}})}{s-n}\ ;$$
$$\frac{\dot{m}}{2} j\omega L_0 \dot{I}_{s-n} + \left(j\omega L_0 + \frac{r}{s} + \frac{1}{js^2\omega C}\right)\dot{I}_s + $$
$$+ \frac{m}{2} j\omega L_0 \dot{I}_{s+n} = \frac{\dot{U}_s}{s} + \frac{\dot{f}_s(t_{\text{in}};\ t_{\text{fin}})}{s}\ ;$$
$$+ \frac{\dot{m}}{2} j\omega L_0 \dot{I}_s + \left(j\omega L_0 + \frac{r}{s+n} + \frac{1}{j(s+n)^2\omega C}\right)\dot{I}_{s+n} + $$
$$+ \frac{\overset{*}{m}}{2} j\omega L_0 \dot{I}_{s+2n} = \frac{\dot{U}_{s+n}}{s+n} + \frac{\dot{f}_{s+n}(t_{\text{in}};\ t_{\text{fin}})}{s+n}\ , \tag{4.13}$$

. . . .

where

$$[\dot{f}_{s+kn}(t_{\text{in}};\ t_{\text{fin}})] =$$
$$= \frac{1}{T}\sum_{\substack{k=-\infty \\ s=1}}^{\infty} [i_\tau(t_{\text{fin}})e^{-j(s+kn)\omega t_{\text{fin}}} - i(t_{\text{in}})e^{-j(s+kn)\omega t_{\text{in}}}] +$$
$$+ \frac{L_0\dot{m}}{2T}\sum_{k=-\infty}^{\infty}\sum_{s=1}^{\infty}[i_\tau(t_{\text{fin}})e^{-j[s+(k+1)n]\omega t_{\text{fin}}} -$$
$$- i_\tau(t_{\text{in}})e^{-j[s+(k+1)n]\omega t_{\text{in}}}] +$$
$$+ \frac{L_0\overset{*}{m}}{2T}\sum_{k=-\infty}^{\infty}\sum_{s=1}^{\infty}[i_\tau(t_{\text{fin}})e^{-j[s+(k-)n]1\omega t_{\text{fin}}} -$$
$$- i_\tau(t_{\text{in}})e^{-j[s+(k-1)n]\omega t_{\text{in}}}] \tag{4.14}$$
$$k = (-\infty,\ \ldots,\ -1,\ 0,\ 1,\ \ldots,\ +\infty).$$

In the equations (4.13), in contrast to equations (1.18) and (1.28), there occur, in the right-hand sides, coefficients of the expansion in a Fourier series of the functions $f(t_{\text{in}})\delta(t_{\text{in}}+nT/2)$ and $f(t_{\text{fin}})\delta(t_{\text{in}}+nT/2)$. Since the initial conditions are assigned, the functions $f(t_{\text{in}})$ are known quantities; the functions $f(t_{\text{fin}})$ must be determined.

In order to determine $f(t_{\text{fin}})$ we shall consider the current in the circuit at an instant of time t lying outside the interval of time τ.

We recall that for an arbitrary instant of time not lying inside the interval τ, the value of the current $i_\tau(t)$ flowing in the circuit and of $u_\tau(t)$, the applied voltage, must by hypothesis be equal to zero everywhere outside the interval τ, except at the boundaries of the interval where the current $i_\tau(t)$ is equal respectively to $i(t_{\text{in}})$ and $i(t_{\text{fin}})$ and the voltage across a capacitor is equal to $u_c(t_{\text{in}})$ and $u_c(t_{\text{fin}})$.

As can be seen from (4.13), in order to ensure that the requirements indicated are met, it has proved necessary to apply, in addition, to the circuit periodic impulse quantities $f(t_{\text{in}})$, generating periodic impulse currents and voltages at the instants of time t_{in} and t_{fin} equal respectively to $i(t_{in})$, $i(t_{\text{fin}})$, $u_c(t_{\text{in}})$ and $u_c(t_{\text{fin}})$ and equal to zero for all other values of t.

The values of $i(t_{\text{fin}})$ and $u_c(t_{\text{fin}})$ can be determined in the following manner. Let us consider the current $i_\tau(t)$ for the case when the additional quantities $i(t_{\text{fin}})$ and $u_c(t_{\text{fin}})$ are not introduced in the equation. Let us denote the corresponding values of current and capacitor voltage by $i_{\tau 0}(t)$ and $u_{c\tau 0}(i)$. The values of $i_{\tau 0}$ (t) and $u_{c\tau 0}$ (t) will no longer be equal to zero outside the interval τ. Their values outside this interval can be expressed in terms of $i(t_{\text{fin}})$ and $u_c(t_{\text{fin}})$.

In fact, the sum of the values of $i_{\tau 0}(t)$ and of the currents caused by the impulses of current and voltage at the instant of time t_{fin}, and respectively the sum of the values of $u_{c\tau 0}(t)$ and of the voltages caused by the impulses of current and voltage at the instant of time t_{fin}, is equal to zero outside the interval τ, and in the interval τ gives corresponding functions of time, coinciding with the functions describing the time behaviour of transient currents and voltages.

In addition, at the instant of time $t = t_{\text{in}} + 0$ the values of $i_{\tau 0}(t)$ and $u_{c\tau 0}(t)$ are equal respectively to $i(t_{in})$ and $u_c(t_{\text{in}})$. From these conditions the values of $i(t_{\text{fin}})$ and $u_c(t_{\text{fin}})$ can be determined.

As an example we shall consider the determination of the values of $i(t_{\text{fin}})$ and $u_c(t_{\text{fin}})$ for a simple oscillatory circuit with variable parameters.

We shall determine the response arising in the circuit when unit periodic voltage impulses occurring at instants of time $t_{\text{fin}} \pm nT/2$ are applied to the circuit. The action of a unit voltage impulse causes the following current and voltage (across the capacitor of the oscillatory circuit)

$$i_{\delta_e}(t) = \frac{2}{T} \operatorname{Re} \sum_{k=-\infty}^{\infty} \sum_{s=1}^{\infty} \frac{e^{-j(s+kn)\omega t_{\text{fin}}}}{Z[(js+jkn)\omega]} e^{j(s+kn)\omega t} =$$

$$= \frac{2}{T} \operatorname{Re} \sum_{k=-\infty}^{\infty} \sum_{s=1}^{\infty} \frac{e^{-j(s+kn)\omega t_{\text{fin}}}}{r + j(s+kn)\omega L + \dfrac{1}{j(s+kn)\omega C}} e^{j(s+kn)\omega t};$$

$$u_{c\delta_e} = \frac{2}{T} \sum_{k=-\infty}^{\infty} \sum_{s=1}^{\infty} \frac{e^{-j(s+kn)\omega t_{\text{fin}}}}{r + j(s+kn)\omega L + \dfrac{1}{j(s+kn)\omega C}} e^{j(s+kn)\omega t} \quad (4.15)$$

The following current and voltage arise respectively due to the action of a unit current impulse

$$i_{\delta_i} = \frac{-2}{T} \operatorname{Re} \sum_{s=1}^{\infty} \sum_{k=-\infty}^{\infty} \frac{e^{-j(s+kn)\omega t_{\text{fin}}}}{r + j(s+kn)\omega L + \dfrac{1}{j(s+kn)\,\omega C}} \times$$

$$\times \frac{1}{j(s+kn)\omega C} e^{j(s+kn)\omega t};$$

$$u_{c\delta_i}(t) = \frac{2}{T} \operatorname{Re} \sum_{s=1}^{\infty} \sum_{k=-\infty}^{\infty} \frac{e^{-j(s+kn)\omega t_{\text{fin}}}}{r + j(s+kn)\omega L + \dfrac{1}{j(s+kn)\omega C}} \times$$

$$\times \frac{r + j(s+kn)\omega L}{j(s+kn)\omega C} e^{j(s+kn)\omega t}. \quad (4.16)$$

We can write for an interval of time lying outside the interval τ (a simple oscillatory circuit)

$$i_{\tau_0}(t) - \omega L \cdot i(t_{\text{fin}}) \cdot i_{\delta_e}(t) + \omega C \cdot u_c(t_{\text{fin}}) i_{\delta_i}(t) = 0;$$

$$u_{c\tau_0}(t) - \omega L \cdot i(t_{\text{fin}}) u_{c\delta_e}(t) - \omega C \cdot u_c(t_{\text{fin}}) u_{c\delta_i}(t) = 0. \qquad (4.17)$$

By putting $t = t_{\text{in}}$ in the equations (4.17) and substituting for $i_{\tau 0}(t)$ and $u_{c\tau 0}(t)$ the known values $i(t_{\text{in}})$ and $u(t_{\text{in}})$, we find $i(t_{\text{fin}})$ and $u_c(t_{\text{fin}})$.

We can find in a similar manner the values of the functions $i(t_{\text{fin}})$ and $u_c(t_{\text{fin}})$ in the general case of a branched circuit, including the case of an infinite iterated circuit corresponding to the system of equations (4.13).

The method of calculation described above leads to the necessity of additional calculations for the determination of the harmonic components of a periodized impulse function corresponding to the term $f(t_{\text{fin}})$. The evaluation of these quantities, which complicates the calculation, can be avoided if an approximate method is used which removes the necessity of evaluating the function $f(t_{\text{fin}})$.

This method consists in introducing in the analysis, instead of the functions $i_\tau(t)$, $u_{c\tau}(t)$, $u_{L\tau}(t)$ and $u_\tau(t)$ the functions

$$i_{\tau,\lambda}(t) = i_\tau(t) e^{-\lambda\tau}; \quad u_{c\tau,\lambda}(t) = u_{c\tau}(t) e^{-\lambda t}; \quad u_{L\tau,\lambda}(t) = u_{L\tau}(t) e^{-\lambda t};$$
$$u_{\tau,\lambda}(t) = u_\tau(t) e^{-\lambda t}. \qquad (4.18)$$

In this way, as above, the complex amplitude of the s-th harmonic of the expansion of the function i_τ, $\lambda(t)$ in a Fourier series will have the following form

$$\dot{I}_{s,\lambda} = \frac{2}{T} \int_0^{T/2} i_\tau(t) e^{-(\lambda + js\omega)t} dt. \qquad (4.19)$$

Accordingly the expression for the complex amplitude of the voltage drop across the inductance will have the following form

$$\dot{U}_{s,\lambda} = \frac{2L}{T}\int_0^{T/2} \frac{d}{dt}[i_\tau(t)]e^{-(\lambda+js\omega)t}\,dt =$$

$$= \frac{2L}{T}\left[i_\tau(t)e^{-(\lambda+js\omega)t}\right]_{t_{\text{in}}}^{t_{\text{fin}}} + (\lambda+js\omega)\frac{2L}{T}\int_0^{T/2} i_\tau e^{-(\lambda+js\omega)t}dt =$$

$$= L(\lambda+js\omega)\dot{I}_{s,\lambda} + \frac{2L}{T}[i_\tau(t_{\text{fin}})e^{-(\lambda+js\omega)t_{\text{fin}}} -$$

$$- i_\tau(t_{\text{in}})e^{-(\lambda+js\omega)t_{\text{in}}}]. \qquad (4.20)$$

i.e. we have obtained an expression similar to (4.4) and differing from it only in that here $j\omega+\lambda$ occurs instead of $j\omega$.

In a similar manner formulae (4.5) and (4.9) are also changed.

Accordingly we obtain, for all the networks considered, equations that differ from the ones obtained earlier only in that $\lambda+j\omega$ occurs everywhere instead of $j\omega$.

By using this method, we can find from (4.15) an expression for the current $i_{\delta_e\lambda}$ flowing in a simple oscillatory circuit through the capacitor at the instant of time $t = t_{\text{in}}$ under the action of a periodic unit voltage impulse acting at the instants of time $t_{\text{fin}} \pm nT/2$. We have here

$$i_{\delta_e\lambda}(t_{\text{in}}) = \frac{2}{T}\operatorname{Re}\sum_{s=1}^{\infty}\frac{e^{-(js\omega+\lambda)t_{\text{fin}}}}{Z(js\omega+\lambda)}\,e^{(js\omega+\lambda)t_{\text{in}}} =$$

$$= \frac{2}{T}\operatorname{Re}\sum_{s=1}^{\infty}\frac{e^{(js\omega+\lambda)\,(t_{\text{in}}-t_{\text{fin}})}}{Z(js\omega+\lambda)} =$$

$$= \frac{2}{T}\operatorname{Re}\sum_{s=1}^{\infty}\frac{e^{(js\omega+\lambda)\,(T/2-\tau)}}{Z(js\omega+\lambda)}. \qquad (4.21)$$

It can be seen from (4.21) that the value of $i_{\delta_e\lambda}(t_{\text{in}})$ will be smaller the larger the value of $T/2-\tau$ and the larger the value of λ. Therefore, with a suitable choice of λ the impulse functions $i(t_{\text{fin}})$ and $u_{c\tau}(t_{\text{fin}})$ can be neglected without introducing any substantial errror.†

† We observe here that, on the other hand, increase of λ also makes the convergence of the series worse.

It can be shown that the replacing of the functions $u_\tau(t)$ and $i_\tau(t)$ by the functions $u_\tau(t)e^{-\lambda t}$ and $i_\tau(t)e^{-\lambda t}$ can be interpreted physically as the replacing of the original network by a network with increased losses to which instead of the voltage $u(t)$ there is applied the voltage $e^{-\lambda t}u(t)$. This is easily verified by comparing the equations of a network with increased losses, in which the losses are increased by connecting resistances $r = \lambda L$ in series with the inductances of the network and conductances $g = \lambda C$ in parallel with the capacitances, with the equations obtained from the equations of the original network after substituting in them $j\omega+\lambda$ for $j\omega$.

We can easily pass from the solution of the equations of the network having its losses increased in such a manner to the solution of the equations of the original network, by multiplying the solutions obtained by $e^{\lambda t}$. The method can be illustrated by the example of a simple circuit consisting of constant inductance, capacitance and resistance. By applying to such a circuit a voltage varying according to a sinusoidal law, the equation connecting the s-th harmonics of current and voltage will have the form

$$r\dot{I}_s + js\omega L\dot{I}_s + \frac{1}{js\omega C}\dot{I}_s = \dot{U}_s + f(t_{\text{in}};\, t_{\text{fin}}). \tag{4.22}$$

Correspondingly, if to the same network, but having resistive impedances λL connected in series with the inductances and resistive conductances λC connected in parallel with the capacitances, there is applied a voltage represented by a periodized segment of an attenuated sinusoid having an attenuation coefficient λ, we obtain, instead of (4.22),

$$js\omega L\dot{I}_{s,\lambda} + \lambda L\dot{I}_{s,\lambda} + rI_{s,\lambda} + \frac{\dot{I}_{s,\lambda}}{js\omega C+\lambda C} = \dot{U}_{s,\lambda} + f_{s,\lambda}(t_{\text{in}};\, t_{\text{fin}}). \tag{4.23}$$

Here $\dot{I}_{s\lambda}$ is the current in the network where additional losses have been introduced in the manner indicated, $\dot{U}_{s\lambda}$ is the s-th harmonic of the periodized voltage applied, being a periodized segment of an attenuated sinusoid with attenuation λ, and $f_{s,\nu}$ (t_{in}; t_{fin}) is the s-th harmonic of the Fourier-series expansion of the impulse function. Here, in the circuit with additional losses, this term is equal to

$$f_{s,\lambda}(t_{\text{in}};\ t_{\text{fin}}) = -\ 2/T\ [i(t_{\text{in}})e^{-(js\omega+\lambda)t_{\text{in}}} -$$
$$-\ i(t_{\text{fin}})e^{-(js\omega+\lambda)t_{\text{fin}}}]. \tag{4.24}$$

Equation (4.23) can be represented in the form

$$L(js\omega + \lambda)\dot{I}_{s,\lambda} + r\dot{I}_{s,\lambda} + \frac{\dot{I}_{s\lambda}}{C(js\omega + \lambda)} =$$
$$= \dot{U}_{s,\lambda} + f_{s,\lambda}(t_{\text{in}};\ t_{\text{fin}}). \tag{4.25}$$

It is easily verified by comparing equations (4.25) and (4.22), that equation (4.25) can be obtained from (4.22) by replacing $js\omega$ by $js\omega + \lambda$ in the left-hand side of (4.22) and by replacing $\dot{U}_s$ and $f_s(t_{\text{in}};\ t_{\text{fin}})$ in the right-hand side by $\dot{U}_{s,\lambda}$ and $f_{s,\lambda}$ (t_{in}; t_{fin}).

We obtain for $\dot{I}_{s,\lambda}$ from (4.25) according to (4.3),

$$\dot{I}_{s,\lambda} = \frac{2}{T} \int_0^{T/2} i_{\tau,\lambda}(t)e^{-(js\omega+\lambda)t}\ dt. \tag{4.26}$$

Having determined the complex amplitudes $\dot{I}_{s,\lambda}$ the current $i_{\tau,\lambda}(t)$ can be found

$$i_{\tau,\lambda}(t) = \frac{1}{2}\ \text{Re} \sum_{s=-\infty}^{\infty} \dot{I}_{s,\lambda}e^{js\omega t}. \tag{4.27}$$

We observe here that in determining $\dot{I}_{s,\lambda}$ we can, approximately, neglect the quantities $i_{s,\lambda}(t_{\text{fin}})$ occurring in the right-hand side of (4.23). In fact, as can be seen from (4.21), the error caused by neglecting the terms containing $i(t_{\text{fin}})$ decreases with increase in λ.

According to (4.21), we can evaluate the magnitude of the error involved in such an approximation. This error is determined by the value of the currents and voltages at the beginning of the period τ (i.e. at the instant of time t_{in}) as are caused by impulses at the end of the previous period (i.e. at the instant of time t_{fin}).

We observe that if the transient has an oscillatory character and the repetition interval has been so chosen that at the end of the interval the values $i(t_{fin})$ are large, then, in the general case, the error introduced by neglecting the impulse functions $f(t_{fin})$ can prove to be large. This may make it necessary to repeat the calculation using other values of λ, τ and $\omega = \omega_{cal}$ where ω_{cal} is the periodization frequency.

It has been assumed above, in considering the application of the Fourier-series method to the analysis of circuits with periodically varying parameters, that the inductance in the oscillatory circuit is varied periodically according to a simple sinusoidal law. We should point out that the Fourier-series method can also be employed in the general case when the inductance of the oscillatory circuit (or the capacitance, or several parameters at the same time) is *an arbitrary function of time*. In fact, if we pass from the consideration of the actual transients occurring in the circuit, to considering a fictitious periodized process, coinciding with the real one over a finite interval, we obtain that for this fictitious periodized process

$$L_{\text{period}}(t) = \operatorname{Re} \sum_{s=0}^{\infty} L_s e^{j(s\omega t+\alpha_s)}.$$

If the actual law of variation of the inductance is $L = \varphi(t)$, L_s will be equal to $(1/T)\int_0^T \varphi(t) \exp(-js\omega t)dt$ where ω is the periodization frequency.

2. Calculations based on the Fourier-series method in practice

The Fourier-series method enables us to reduce the investigation of transients occurring in electrical circuits to the analysis of alternating-current steady-state processes, arising under the action of the individual harmonics of the e.m.f. and of additional e.m.f.'s depending upon the value of the required quantities at the boundaries of the chosen interval of time of the periodized function. If the approximate method is employed, the e.m.f.'s depending upon the values of the required quantities at the end of the interval can be neglected, as has been shown.

In practice the calculations can be divided into the following stages: (1) the determination of the frequency characteristic of the system investigated, (2) the choice of the parameters τ and λ, and (3) the evaluation of the complex amplitudes of the required quantities and the plotting of curves describing the time behaviour of the transients considered.

3. The choice of the parameters

As the exact calculation procedure by the Fourier-series method is fairly complicated, owing to the necessity of determining in addition the values of the required functions at the instant $t = t_{\text{fin}}$, one uses the approximate procedure for practical calculations.

In the case of a strongly attenuated system, the terms with values of the functions at the instant $t = t_{\text{fin}}$ can be neglected. In addition, if the solutions thus obtained do not satisfy the initial conditions, the functions occurring in the equations are multiplied by the attenuating factor $e^{-\lambda t}$ where λ is an additional attenuation coefficient. As a result of this, in the equations for the coefficients of the harmonics the quantity $js\omega$ is changed into $j\omega s+\lambda$. The introduction of the factor $e^{-\lambda t}$ can be interpreted as the result of connecting in series with each inductance an additional resistance $r_L = \lambda L$ and in parallel with each capacitance a conductance $g_c = \lambda C$.

When the method is used in practice, the interval τ, the fundamental periodization frequency f_{cal} and the attenuation factor λ must be correctly chosen. The magnitude of the interval τ can be roughly estimated from the capacitance and the inductance of the network.

The free-oscillation periods of the network satisfy the inequality $(L_{\min} C_{\min})^{-1/2} > f_{\text{free}} > (L_{\max} C_{\max})^{-1/2}$. In the first version of the calculation, τ must be so chosen as to include the free oscillations of interest to us (either all or a portion of them).

In order to detect high frequencies superimposed on lower ones, τ is chosen at first sufficiently small, and then, when the general character of the process is investigated, τ is chosen sufficiently large in order that it shall include all low-frequency oscillations. The fundamental periodization frequency $f_{cal} = 1/T_{cal}$ is so chosen that over the interval $T/2-\tau$ the processes shall have time to die out. To this end $T/2-\tau$ is chosen sufficiently large; then, after introducing λ, the neglecting of terms depending on the value of the function at the instant $t = t_{fin}$ will not lead to noticeable errors. The value of the frequency f should not coincide with any of the sharp resonant frequencies of the network (nor should it be a multiple of any of them), since in that case neglecting the terms indicated above amounts to neglecting impulse forces acting at resonance with one of the natural frequencies. In all cases the value of τ must be less than $T/2$.

In the presence of sinusoidal disturbances (either with or without attenuation) it often proves convenient, from the viewpoint of making the calculations easier, to choose $T = 4\tau$. The choice of a suitable value of ω_{cal} is made easier by the fact that the value of ω_{cal} and that of λ can be varied at the same time.

At the same time the value of λ must not be chosen too large, to avoid obtaining a series converging too slowly. Also the quantity $f(t_{fin})\exp[-\lambda(T/2-\tau)]$ should not exceed a few per cent of $f(t_{in})$. In the calculation of short-circuit current transients λ is usually taken equal to 0.5.

4. The determination of the complex amplitudes of the applied e.m.f.

In the calculation of a transient process by the Fourier-series method one has to introduce in the equation, instead of the applied disturbances, the expansion of these in a Fourier series over the interval of time considered. If the applied e.m.f. is sinusoidal, this is replaced by the Fourier-series expansion of a segment of sinusoid, taken over the interval assigned and then periodized. If the approximate method is used (by introducing an attenuation) one has to expand correspondingly, instead of a segment of sinusoid $e(t) = \sin(x\omega t+\varphi)$, a segment of the function $e^*(t) = e^{-\lambda\Theta}\sin(x\Theta+\varphi)$. Here the integer x indicates by how many times the frequency of the sinusoid expanded in series is larger than the periodization frequency.

CHAPTER V

METHODS FOR THE ANALYSIS OF PULSE CIRCUITS AND PROBLEMS OF THE THEORY OF PULSE AND DIGITAL AUTOMATIC CONTROLLERS

1. General considerations

The analysis of processes in pulse circuits can be carried out by means of the ordinary methods which are used in the analysis of processes in linear electrical circuits and which are based on the Laplace transformation and on frequency-analysis methods.

In the general case, the investigation of processes in pulse circuits can be carried out proceeding from the consideration of an impulse function as a result of amplitude modulation. In this way expressions can be obtained that enable us to determine the values of all the system quantities both at the instant of a pulse and during a pause between pulses.[10, 16–18]

In pulse code systems the pulse width is usually small in comparison with the time constant of the system. This enables us to introduce certain assumptions that simplify the investigation in comparison with the general case indicated.

When processes in pulse code systems are considered, we are interested in the values of the functions at the instants of time 0, T, $2T$, . . . , nT only, where T is the period between pulses. In this connection, by bearing in mind the relation between the width of a pulse and the interval between pulses, we can assume, approximately, that the values of the functions are characterized by the pulse amplitude only and are identically equal to zero in the interval between pulses. The assumption made can be illustrated by Fig. 3, where a continuous input function and a series of equally spaced pulses into which the function is transformed in passing through a pulser are shown.

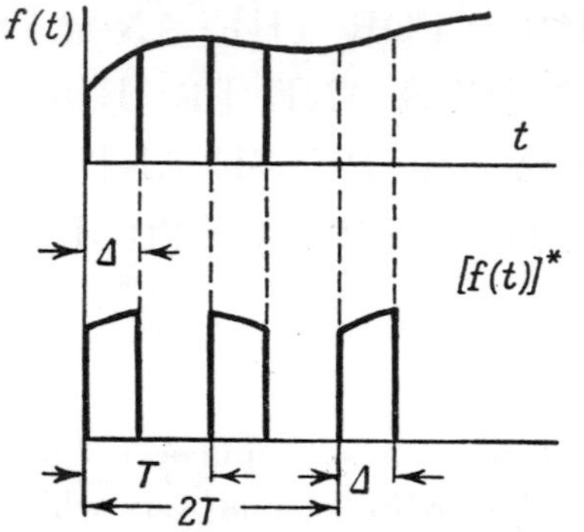

FIG. 3. The impulse function $[f(t)]^*$

2. The use of the Laplace transformation for impulse functions

Let us consider a series of pulses of finite width, equal to Δ, and of finite amplitude, and separated from each other by an interval of time T. Let the envelope of these pulses be a continuous function of time $f(t)$ (Fig. 3). If we denote the pulse function by $f^*(t)$, we can write for $f^*(t)$ the following analytical expression

$$f^*(t) = [f(0)\,1(t) - f(\Delta)1(t-\Delta)] + [f(T)1(t-T) - f(T+ \\ + \Delta)1(t-T-\Delta)] + \dots + [f(nT)\,1(t-nT) - f(nT+\Delta)\,1(t- \\ - nT - \Delta)] = \sum_{n=0}^{n} [f(nT)\,1(t-nT) - f(nT+\Delta)\,1(t-nT-\Delta)]. \tag{5.1}$$

By taking the transforms of both sides of the expression (5.1) (see Table 1, line 3), we obtain

$$F^*(p) = \left[\frac{f(0)}{p} - \frac{f(\Delta)e^{-p\Delta}}{p}\right] +$$

$$+\left[\frac{1}{p}f(T)e^{-pT} - \frac{1}{p}f(T+\Delta)e^{-p(T+\Delta)}\right] +$$

$$+\left[\frac{1}{p}f(2T)e^{-p2T} - \frac{1}{p}f(2T+\Delta)e^{-p(2T+\Delta)}\right] + \dots +$$

$$+\left[\frac{1}{p}f(nT)e^{-pnT} - \frac{1}{p}f(nT+\Delta)e^{-p(nT+\Delta)}\right] =$$

$$= \sum_{n=0}^{n}\frac{1}{p}e^{-pnT}\left[f(nT) - f(nT+\Delta)e^{-p\Delta}\right]. \qquad (5.2)$$

If it is assumed, as has been indicated above, that Δ is sufficiently small and that accordingly $f(kT) \cong f(kT+\Delta)$, expression (5.2) can be rewritten in this case in the form

$$F^*(p) = f(0)\left[\frac{1-e^{-p\Delta}}{p}\right] + f(T)e^{-pT}\left[\frac{1-e^{-p\Delta}}{p}\right] + \dots +$$

$$+f(nT)e^{-npT}\left[\frac{1-e^{-p\Delta}}{p}\right] = \left[\frac{1-e^{-p\Delta}}{p}\right][f(0)+e^{-pT}f(T)+$$

$$+e^{-2pT}f(2T)+ \dots +e^{-npT}f(nT)] = V\sum_{k=0}^{n} e^{-kpT}f(kT), \qquad (5.3)$$

where

$$V = \frac{1-e^{-p\Delta}}{p}.$$

It proves possible in a number of cases to sum the infinite series occurring in expression (5.3); thus an expression for $F^*(p)$ can be obtained in closed form.

As an example of the application of formula (5.3) leading to an expression in closed form, we shall consider the particular case $f^*(t) = [e^{-at}]^*$ (Fig. 4).

Formula (5.3) can be rewritten, for this particular case, in the form

$$F^*(p) = [1+e^{-pT}e^{-aT}+e^{-2pT}e^{-a2T}+\ldots+$$
$$+e^{-pkT}e^{-akT}+\ldots]\left[\frac{1-e^{-p\Delta}}{p}\right]. \tag{5.4}$$

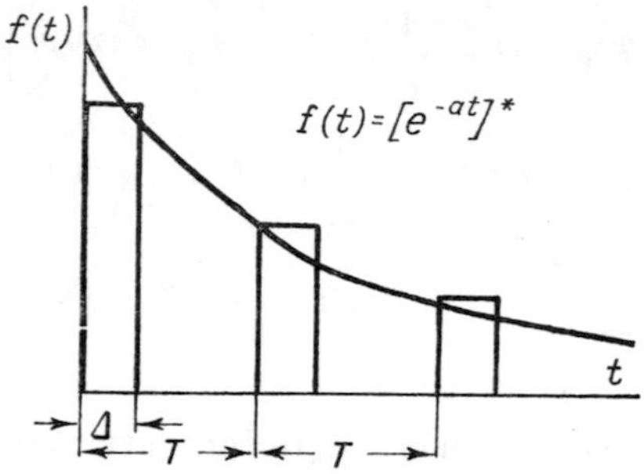

FIG. 4. The impulse function $[e^{-at}]^*$

We observe that the infinite series occurring in the expression (5.4) is a geometric progression having common ratio $e^{-(p+a)T}$. On summing the progression indicated we obtain

$$F^*(p) = \frac{1}{1-e^{-(p+a)T}}V = \frac{e^{pT}}{e^{pT}-e^{-aT}}V. \tag{5.5}$$

3. The z-transformation

We have considered in the preceding sections the Laplace transforms and the frequency characteristics of impulse functions. As can be seen from the formulae (5.2) and (5.5) these transforms are transcendental functions of the operator p, or more exactly are functions of e^{-pT}. In the case when $\Delta \to 0$ while the amplitude tends to infinity we can, to simplify the notation, make the following substitution†

$$e^{-pT} = z^{-1}. \tag{5.6}$$

† Such a substitution corresponds to a conformal transformation of the plane of the complex frequencies (the p-plane) for which the left-hand

We pass by means of such a substitution from the Laplace transform of the impulse function $F^*(p)$ to the function $F(z)$ which we call the z-transform of the impulse function $f^*(t)$.

The functions $F(z)$, for impulse functions of time as are met in practice, are rational functions of z, which fact makes their investigation much easier in comparison with the investigation of transcendental functions in the p-plane.

As an example, we shall find the z-transforms of a number of functions most often encountered in practical applications.

An expression in closed form has been obtained above for the function $f^*(t) = [e^{-at}]^*$. We have for this function for $V = 1$ (see § 4, Chapter V)

$$F^*(p) = \frac{1}{1-e^{-aT}e^{-pT}}, \tag{5.7}$$

whence, after substituting in (5.7) $e^{-pT} = z^{-1}$ we obtain

$$F^*(z) = \frac{1}{1-e^{-aT}z^{-1}}. \tag{5.7'}$$

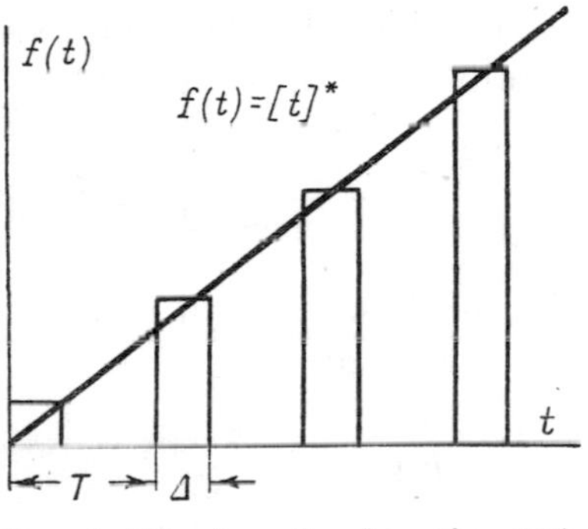

FIG. 5. The impulse function $[t]^*$

We shall also derive an expression for the impulse function $f^*(t) = [t]^*$ (Fig. 5). At the instants of time 0, T, $2T$, . . . etc.

half-plane of the p-plane is transformed in the z-plane into the inner region of a circle of unit radius, the imaginary p-axis into the boundary of this circle and the right-hand half-plane of the p-plane into the external region of this circle.

this function assumes the value $f(0)$, $f(T)$, $f(2T)$ etc., retains this value during an interval of time Δ and is equal to zero at all remaining instants of time. The Laplace transform of this function will be equal to

$$F^*(p) = Te^{-pT}+2Te^{-2pT}+\dots . \tag{5.8}$$

By carrying out the substitution $e^{-pT} = z^{-1}$ we obtain

$$F(z) = \frac{T}{z}+\frac{2T}{z^2}+\frac{3T}{z^3}+\dots \tag{5.9}$$

or

$$\frac{F(z)}{zT} = \frac{1}{z^2}+\frac{2}{z^3}+\frac{3}{z^4}+\dots . \tag{5.10}$$

By multiplying both sides by dz and integrating, we obtain

$$\int \frac{F(z)}{zT}\,dz = -\frac{1}{z}-\frac{1}{z^2}-\frac{1}{z^3}-,\dots,+k; \tag{5.11}$$

by taking $(-1/z)$ outside the brackets and summing the progression we obtain

$$\int \frac{F(z)}{zT}\,dz = \frac{-1}{(z-1)}+k. \tag{5.12}$$

On differentiating both sides with respect to z and solving with respect to $F(z)$ we obtain

$$F(z) = \frac{zT}{(z-1)^2}\cdot \tag{5.13}$$

The z-transforms of other functions can be found in a similar manner. A short summary of z-transforms of certain functions most often encountered is shown in the third column of Table 1.

It must be pointed out that the inverse passage from $F(z)$ to the function $f(t)$ is not uniquely defined, just as the inverse passage from $F^*(p)$ to $f(t)$ is not a single-valued operation.

z-TRANSFORMS OF SIMPLE FUNCTIONS TABLE 1

Laplace transform	*Time function*	*z-transform*
1	$\delta(t)$	1
$\dfrac{1}{p}$	$1\,(t)$	$\dfrac{z}{z-1}$
$\dfrac{e^{-nTp}}{p}$	$1(t-T_n)$	$\dfrac{1}{z^n}$
$F(p+a)$	$e^{-at}f(t)$	$F(e^{+at}z)$
$\dfrac{1}{p^2}$	t	$\dfrac{Tz}{(z-1)^2}$
$\dfrac{1}{p^3}$	$\dfrac{1}{2}t^2$	$\dfrac{1}{2}T^2\dfrac{z(z+1)}{(z-1)^2}$
$\dfrac{1}{p+a}$	e^{-at}	$\dfrac{z}{z-e^{-aT}}$
$\dfrac{a}{p^2+a^2}$	$\sin at$	$\dfrac{z \sin aT}{z^2-2z\cos aT+1}$
$\dfrac{1}{p-(1/T)\ln a}$	$a^{t/T}$	$\dfrac{z}{z-a}$
$\dfrac{b}{[p-(1/T)\ln a]^2+b^2}$	$a^{t/T}\sin bt$	$\dfrac{za \sin bT}{z^2-2az\cos bT+a^2}$
$\dfrac{p-(1/T)\ln a}{[p-(1(T)\ln a]^2-b^2}$	$a^{t/T}\cos bt$	$\dfrac{z(z-a\cos bT)}{z^2-2az\cos bT+a^2}$

This is connected with the fact that the z-transforms (or the p-transforms) of two different functions coinciding at the instants of time 0, T, $2T$, . . . , will be equal to each other.

4. Frequency characteristics of impulse functions

Let us consider in some detail certain general properties of the frequency characteristics of impulse functions. We observe that instead of the expression (5.1) we can write for the impulse function $f^*(t)$ the following equivalent expression

$$f^*(t) = f(t)\,[1(t)]^*, \tag{5.14}$$

where

$$[1(t)]^* = [1(t)-1(t-\Delta)]+\{1(t-T)-1[t-(T+\Delta)]\}+ \\ +\ldots+\{1(t-T)-1[t-(nT+\Delta)]\}. \tag{5.15}$$

By using the expansion theorem the function $[1(t)]^*$ can be represented in the following form[†]

$$[1(t)]^* = L^{-1}\left[\frac{1}{1-e^{-pT}}\right] = \sum_{k=0}^{n}\frac{A_1(p_k)}{B_1'(p_k)}e^{p_k t}; \tag{5.16}$$

where p_k are the poles of the function $L[1(t)]$, which are situated at the points $p_k = jn\omega_{\text{per}}$, where $\omega_{\text{per}} = 2\pi/T$ is the periodization frequency.

Bearing in mind (5.16) and taking the z-transforms of both sides of (5.14), we can write the following equality

$$F^*(p) = L[f(t)1^*(t)] = L[f(t)\sum_{k=0}^{n}\frac{A_1(p_k)}{B_1'(p_k)}e^{p_k t}], \tag{5.17}$$

whence, by using the displacement theorem, we obtain finally

$$F^*(p) = \sum_{k=0}^{n}\frac{A_1(p_k)}{B_1'(p_k)}L[f(t)e^{p_k t}] = \sum_{k=0}^{n}\frac{A_1(p_k)}{B_1'(p_k)}F(p-p_k). \tag{5.18}$$

Bearing in mind that in the case given the residues at the poles of $1(p)$ are equal to $1/T$ while the poles p_k are situated at the points $jn\omega_{\text{per}}$ (where n are integers from $-\infty$ to $+\infty$, i.e. $p_k = jn\omega_{\text{per}}$), we can rewrite the relation (5.18) in the form

$$F^*(p) = \sum_{n=-\infty}^{\infty}\frac{A_1(jn\omega_{\text{per}})}{B_1'(jn\omega_{\text{per}})}F(p+jn\omega_{\text{per}}). \tag{5.19}$$

Expression (5.19) shows that the frequency characteristic of an impulse function is a periodic function of ω with period

† M. F. Gardner and T. L. Barnes; *Transients in Linear Systems* (1942).

$T = 2\pi/\omega_{per}$, i.e.

$$F^*(p+jm\omega_{per}) = F^*(p).$$

In fact, if we replace p in (5.19) by $p+jm\omega_{per}$, all the p_k will at the same time change and will assume the values $p_k+jm\omega_{per} = j(n+m)\omega_{per}$, whence

$$F(p+jm\omega_{per}) = \sum_{m,n=-\infty}^{\infty} \frac{A_1[j(n+m)\omega_{per}}{B_1'[j(n+m)\omega_{per}]} F(p+j(n+m)\omega_{per}] =$$

$$= \sum_{k=-\infty}^{\infty} \frac{A_1(jn\omega_{per})}{B_1'(jn\omega_{per})} F(p+jn\omega_{per}) = F^*(p). \qquad (5.20)$$

Expression (5.14) can be represented in a somewhat different form. If we take into account that $[1(t)]^*$ is a periodic function of time with period equal to T and expand this function in a Fourier series, we obtain for the coefficient of the Fourier series

$$F(\omega) = \frac{1}{T}\int_0^{\triangle} [1(t)]^* e^{-j\omega t} dt = \frac{1}{T}\left| \frac{e^{-j\omega t}}{j\omega} \right|_0^{\triangle} =$$

$$= \frac{1}{T}\frac{1-e^{-j\omega\triangle}}{j\omega} = \frac{V(j\omega)}{T}. \qquad (5.21)$$

We can write, on the basis of (5.21),

$$L\{f(t)[1(t)]^*\} = \frac{1}{T} V(j\omega) \sum_{n=-\infty}^{\infty} F(p-jn\omega_{per}) =$$

$$= \frac{V(j\omega)}{T} \sum_{n=-\infty}^{\infty} F(p+jn\omega_{per}). \qquad (5.21a)$$

In a number of cases, when pulses of very small width and very great height are applied, we can obtain, instead of (5.21a) a simpler expression. It proves convenient in this case to represent the function $f^*(t)$ instead of as (5.14) in the form

$$f^*(t) = f(t)\,\delta_T(t),$$

where

$$\delta_T(t) = \sum_{k=-\infty}^{\infty} F(\omega) e^{jk\omega_{\text{per}} t} \tag{5.22}$$

is the periodized δ-function. The function $\delta_T(t)$ represents a series of pulses of infinitely small width and infinitely great height, separated from each other by the interval T, the area of each pulse being equal to unity. If we take the width of each of the pulses indicated as equal to Δ and the height of a pulse as equal to $1/\Delta$, then in the limit as $\Delta \to 0$ each of such pulses will represent a δ-function. Correspondingly, a whole series of similar pulses, repeated periodically after an interval of time T, will represent a periodized δ-function, i.e. the function $\delta_T(t)$.

In the case given the coefficients of the Fourier-series expansion are somewhat simpler in comparison with (5.20).

According to the definition of δ-function the coefficients of its Fourier-series expansion will be equal to

$$F(\omega) = \frac{1}{T} \lim_{\Delta \to 0} \int_0^{\Delta} \frac{1}{\Delta} e^{-jk\omega_{\text{per}} t}\, dt = \frac{1}{T} \lim_{\Delta \to 0} \left| -\frac{e^{-jk\omega_{\text{per}} t}}{j\omega\Delta} \right|_0^{\Delta} =$$

$$= \frac{1}{T} \lim_{\Delta \to 0} \frac{1 - \cos k\omega\Delta - j \sin k\omega\Delta}{j\omega\Delta} = \frac{1}{T}. \tag{5.23}$$

It follows from (5.22) and (5.23) that

$$\delta_T(t) = \frac{1}{T} \sum_{n=-\infty}^{\infty} e^{jn\omega_{\text{per}} t}$$

and correspondingly

$$F^*(p) = L[f(t)]\,\delta_T(t) = \frac{1}{T} \sum_{n=-\infty}^{\infty} L[f(t) e^{jn\omega_{\text{per}} t}] =$$

$$= \frac{1}{T} \sum_{n=-\infty}^{\infty} F(p - jn\omega_{\text{per}}) = \frac{1}{T} \sum_{n=-\infty}^{\infty} F(p + jn\omega_{\text{per}}). \tag{5.24}$$

On the basis of (5.24) we can directly write the following identity

$$[F(p+jk\omega_{\text{per}})]^* = F^*(p). \tag{5.25}$$

We observe in conclusion that the expressions obtained from formula (5.22) differ from the expressions obtained from formula (5.14) in that the factor $V(j\omega)$ (or respectively $V(p)$, is absent. *We shall use below these simpler expressions, bearing in mind that, in case of necessity, the factor* $V(j\omega)$ *can always be introduced.*

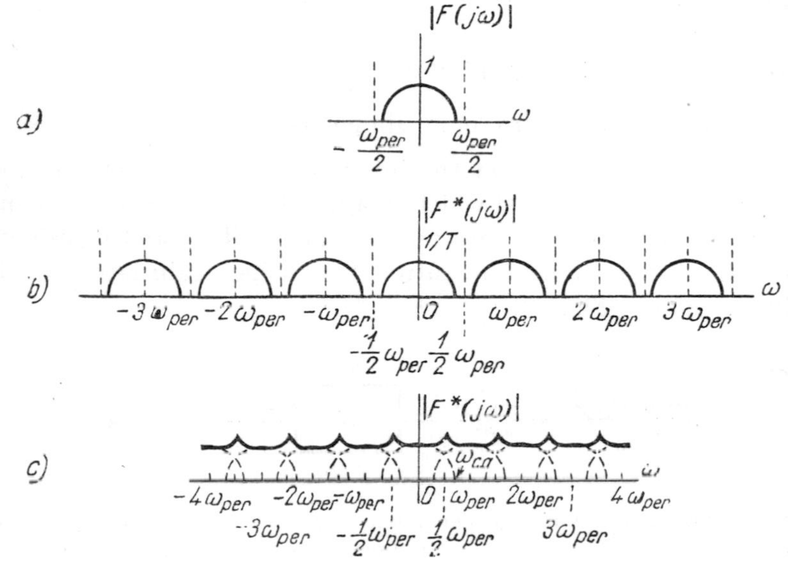

FIG. 6. Frequency characteristics of impulse functions

If the transform of the input signal has an amplitude-frequency characteristic the bandwidth of which is smaller than half the frequency of the pulser, as is indicated in Fig. 6,*a*, then the amplitude-frequency characteristic of the signal at the output of the pulser is a multiply-repeated copy of the amplitude-frequency characteristic of the input signal with the amplitude values decreased in the ratio $1/T$, as is shown in

Fig. 6,*b*. In this case, in addition to the frequencies contained in the input signal, i.e. in addition to the fundamental frequencies, the output signal will contain an infinite number of sideband frequencies. Physically this is due to the fact that the connecting and disconnecting of the pulser can be considered as a modulation of the applied e.m.f. at a frequency equal to the frequency of the pulser. We observe that in the case when the $\omega_{\text{cut-off}}$ of the signal is larger than half the ω of the pulser, the input signal is distorted and cannot be directly isolated by means of linear filters from the output signal Fig. 6,*c*).

5. System functions of pulse circuits

(a) System functions of a simple circuit

Let us suppose that at the input of an electrical circuit an input voltage is applied which, via a pulser, is connected to an element of the circuit with transfer factor $W(p)$ and transient function $g(t)$, the output quantity Δx_{out} being again interrupted by a pulser (Fig. 7).

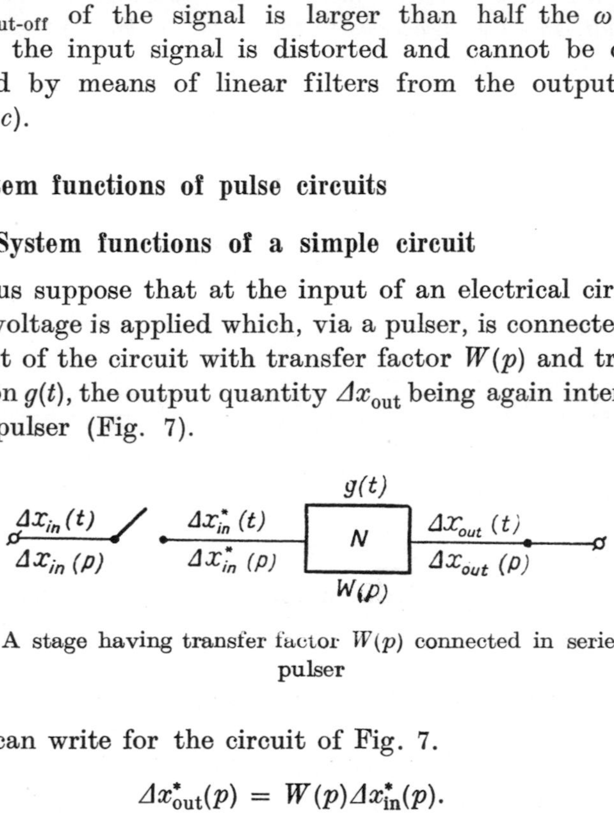

FIG. 7. A stage having transfer factor $W(p)$ connected in series with a pulser

We can write for the circuit of Fig. 7.

$$\Delta x^*_{\text{out}}(p) = W(p)\Delta x^*_{\text{in}}(p). \tag{5.26}$$

We obtain accordingly for the quantity $\Delta x_{\text{out}}(p)$, by taking into account (5.24),

$$\Delta x^*_{\text{out}}(p) = \frac{1}{T} \sum_{n=-\infty}^{\infty} W(p+jn\omega_{\text{per}})\Delta x_{\text{in}}(p+jn\omega_{\text{per}}). \tag{5.27}$$

By bearing in mind that according to (5.25) $\Delta x_{\text{in}}(p+jn\omega_{\text{per}}) = \Delta x^*_{\text{out}}(p)$, we obtain

$$\Delta x^*_{\text{out}}(p) = [\Delta x^*_{\text{in}}(p)W(p)]^* = \Delta x^*_{\text{in}}(p)W^*(p),$$

where

$$W^*(p) = \frac{1}{T}\sum_{n=-\infty}^{\infty} W(p+jn\omega_{\text{per}}). \tag{5.28}$$

That is, by introducing a suitable notation (namely the symbol*) we obtain for pulse circuits a relation between the input quantity $\Delta x^*_{\text{in}}(p)$ and the output quantity $\Delta x^*_{\text{out}}(p)$ which is similar to the usual relation for linear continuous circuits. However, in contrast to the usual linear continuous circuits, all operational quantities are here infinite sums, connected with the corresponding functions of a linear continuous circuit by the relation (5.3), or (5.20), or (5.24). Just this connection is indicated by the sign*. Depending on what the input and output quantities are, the system function $W^*(p)$ can characterize either the input properties (the input impedance or input admittance) or the transfer properties of the circuit, i.e. can represent either the input impedance U_1^*/I_1^* (the input admittance I_1^*/U_1^*) or the transfer factor U_1^*/U_2^* (I_1^*/I_2^*) or the transfer impedance or conductance, i.e. U_1^*/I_2^* or I_1^*/U_2^*.

In real systems in which the function $W(j\omega)$ tends to zero as $\omega \to \infty$, we can restrict ourselves in the expression (5.28) for $W^*(j\omega)$ to a finite number of terms.

The quantity $W^*(p)$, just as the quantity $W(p)$, is closely connected with the frequency characteristic and the impulse characteristics of the circuit.

Let the input quantity be equal to $\Delta x_{\text{in}}(t) = e^{at}$, then, according to (5.22) and (5.24),

$$\Delta x^*_{\text{in}}(t) = e^{at} \cdot \delta_{\text{T}}(t) = \frac{1}{T}\sum_{n=-\infty}^{\infty} e^{(a+jn\omega_{\text{per}})t} \tag{5.29}$$

and correspondingly

$$\Delta x_{\text{out}}(t) = \frac{1}{T} \sum_{n=-\infty}^{\infty} W(a+jn\omega_{\text{per}}) e^{(a+jn\omega_{\text{per}})t} =$$

$$= \frac{1}{T} W(D) \sum_{n=-\infty}^{\infty} e^{(a+jn\omega_{\text{per}})t}; \; D = \frac{dt}{d}. \tag{5.30}$$

After the output signal $\Delta x_{\text{out}}(t)$ has passed through the pulser, we obtain at the output of the pulser the signal $\Delta x^*_{\text{out}}(t)$. By taking into account (5.14) for $\Delta x^*_{\text{out}}(t)$, we obtain the expression†

$$\Delta x^*_{\text{out}}(t) = \Delta x_{\text{out}}(t)\,\delta_T(t) = [W^*(a)e^{at}]\,\delta_T(t), \tag{5.31}$$

where $\delta_T(t)$ is the unit impulse function. It follows from (5.31) that $[W^*(a)e^{at}]\delta_T(t)$ is the envelope of the output response of the system (Fig. 7) to an input disturbance of the type e^{at}. Thus the impulse transfer function $W^*(p)$ connects the input function $\Delta x^*_{\text{in}}(p)$ and the Laplace transform of the envelope of the impulse output $\Delta x^*_{\text{out}}(p)$, just as the transfer function $W(p)$ connects the input function $\Delta x_{\text{in}}(p)$ with the output function $\Delta x_{\text{out}}(p)$ in the case of continuous operation.

Another important property of the function $W^*(p)$ can be established by considering the response of an impulse circuit to a unit step. If the response of the element N (Fig. 7) to a unit step, i.e. its transient characteristic, is equal to $g(t)$, then, according to (5.14), $W^*(p) = L[g(t)1^*(t)]$ or, according to (5.22)

$$W^*(p) = L[g(t).\,\delta_T(t)]$$

We should bear in mind that in the case of pulse circuits in the expression for the transfer factor complex coefficients will occur.

† We are here taking into account that

$$\Delta x^*_{\text{out}}(t) = \Delta x_{\text{out}}(t)\,\delta_T(t) = W(D)e^{at} \sum_{n=-\infty}^{\infty} e^{jn\omega_{\text{per}}t} \sum_{n=-\infty}^{\infty} e^{jm\omega_{\text{per}}t} =$$

$$= W(D)e^{at} \sum_{n,m} e^{j(n+m)\omega_{\text{per}}t} = W(D)\,e^{at} \sum_{n=-\infty}^{\infty} e^{jn\omega_{\text{per}}t} = W(a+jn\omega_{\text{per}})e^{at}\,\delta_T(t) =$$

$$= W^*(a)e^{at}\,\delta_T(t).$$

(b) System functions of complex impulse circuits

Let us consider the expression for the impulse transfer function of two four-pole networks connected in series.

If the circuit consists of two series-connected directional quadrupoles having transfer factors equal respectively to $W_1(p)$ and $W_2(p)$, the overall transfer factor will be equal to

$$W(p) = W_1(p)W_2(p). \tag{5.32}$$

If at the output of the second quadrupole considered a pulser is connected in series, the resulting impulse transfer function will be equal to

$$W^*(p) = \frac{1}{T}\sum_{n=-\infty}^{\infty} W_1(p+jn\omega_{\text{per}})W_2(p+jn\omega_{\text{per}}), \tag{5.33}$$

which will be denoted briefly by

$$W^*(p) = W_1W_2^*(p). \tag{5.34}$$

We observe that the impulse transfer function $W^*(p)$ of two series-connected quadrupoles *is not equal to the product of the impulse transfer function of the individual quadrupoles* (since $\Sigma\Pi W_1W_2 \neq \Sigma W_1\Sigma W_2$).

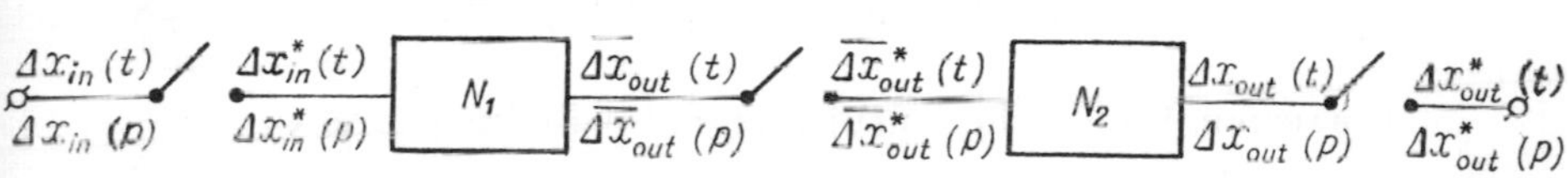

FIG. 8. To determine the impulse transfer factor of two stages separated by pulsers

On the other hand, if the series-connected quadrupoles are separated by a pulser then, by using the notation of Fig. 8, we can write

$$\Delta x^*_{\text{out}}(p) = W_2^*(p)\overline{\Delta}x^*_{\text{out}}(p) \text{ and } \overline{\Delta}x^*_{\text{out}}(p) = W_1^*(p)\Delta x^*_{\text{in}}(p), \tag{5.35}$$

whence

$$\Delta x^*{}_{\text{out}}(p) = W_1^*(p)W_2^*(p)\Delta x^*_{\text{in}}(p) \tag{5.36}$$

and correspondingly

$$W^*(p) = W_1^*(p)W_2^*(p), \tag{5.37}$$

i.e. *the impulse transfer function of two quadrupoles, connected in series via a pulser, is equal to the product of the impulse functions of the individual quadrupoles.*

We can obtain in a similar manner the transfer factors for more complicated networks of pulse circuits.

We shall consider as an example the negative-feedback circuit shown in Fig. 9

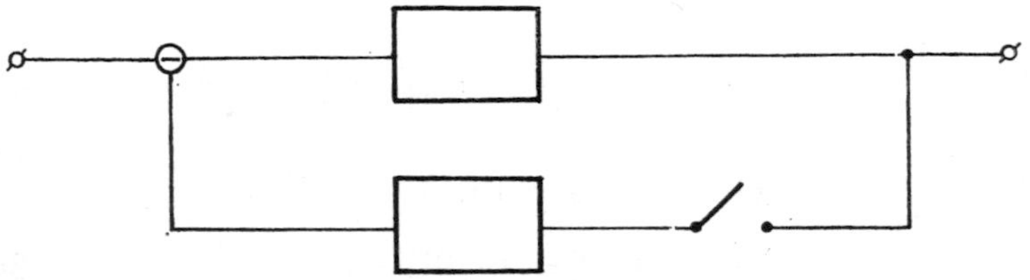

FIG. 9. To determine the impulse transfer factor of a feedback circuit, containing a pulser in the feedback loop

We can write for the input signal, on the basis of Fig. 9,

$$\Delta x_{\text{in}}(p) = F(p) - W_2(p)\Delta x^*_{\text{out}}(p). \tag{5.38}$$

Correspondingly the output signal will be equal to

$$\Delta x_{\text{out}}(p) = W_1(p)\Delta x_{\text{in}}(p). \tag{5.39}$$

On substituting in (5.38) the value of $\Delta x_{\text{in}}(p)$ from (5.39), we obtain

$$\Delta x_{\text{out}}(p) = W_1(p)F(p) - W_1(p)W_2(p)\Delta x^*_{\text{out}}(p). \tag{5.40}$$

By passing from (5.40) to the corresponding impulse function we obtain [on the basis of (5.24) and the following]

$$\Delta x^*_{\text{out}}(p) = W_1F^*(p) - W_1W_2^*(p)\Delta x^*_{\text{out}}(p), \tag{5.41}$$

whence

$$\Delta x^*_{\text{out}}(p) = \frac{W_1 F^*(p)}{1 + W_1 W_2^*(p)}. \tag{5.42}$$

By substituting in (5.42) and (5.40) we obtain

$$\Delta x_{\text{out}}(p) = W_1(p)\left[F(p) - \frac{W_2(p) W_1 F^*(p)}{1 + W_1 W_2^*(p)}\right]. \tag{5.43}$$

We can find, by using similar arguments, the transfer factors of other complex pulse circuits also. Expressions for $\Delta x^*_{\text{out}}(p)$ of a few common feedback circuits are shown in Table 2. The transfer factors can be easily found on the basis of the corresponding $\Delta x^*_{\text{out}}(p)$ when these are known.

6. The determination of the value of the system response to an impulse disturbance at instants of time between impulses

As has been shown above, the signal $\Delta x_{\text{in}}(t)$ represents a series of impulses following one another at an interval of time of T sec. The Laplace transform of this signal $\Delta x^*_{\text{in}}(p)$ and the corresponding z-transform $\Delta x^*_{\text{in}}(z)$ contain in themselves all the information that is contained in $\Delta x^*_{\text{in}}(t)$.

However $W(z)$ or $W^*(p)$ cannot provide a complete representation of the function $\Delta x_{\text{out}}(t)$, since $\Delta x_{\text{out}}(t)$, in contrast to $\Delta x^*_{\text{in}}(t)$, is a function existing not only at the instants of time 0, T, $2T$ etc. but also at the instants of time in the intervals between them, e.g. at the instants of time 0, rT, $2rT$ etc. where r is not an integer.

In the examples, shown above, of application of the Laplace transformation and the corresponding z-transformation to discrete functions we have not considered the problem of the determination of the values of the system response at instants of time between the instants of existence of the impulses.

Below, a method is given which enables us to determine the values of the system response to an impulse disturbance at instants of time T, $T+T_x$, $2T+T_x$, . . . , that are displaced

TABLE 2. IMPULSE TRANSFER FACTORS OF FEEDBACK SYSTEMS, COMPRISING PULSERS[18]

Tipe of circuit	$\Delta x^*_{\text{out}}(p)$	$\Delta x_{\text{out}}(z)$
	$\Delta x^*_{\text{in}}(p)$	$\Delta x_{\text{in}}(z)$
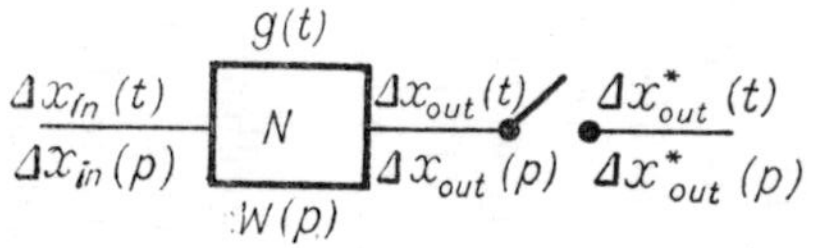	$W_1 \Delta x^*_{\text{in}}(p)$	$W_1 \Delta x_{\text{in}}(z)$
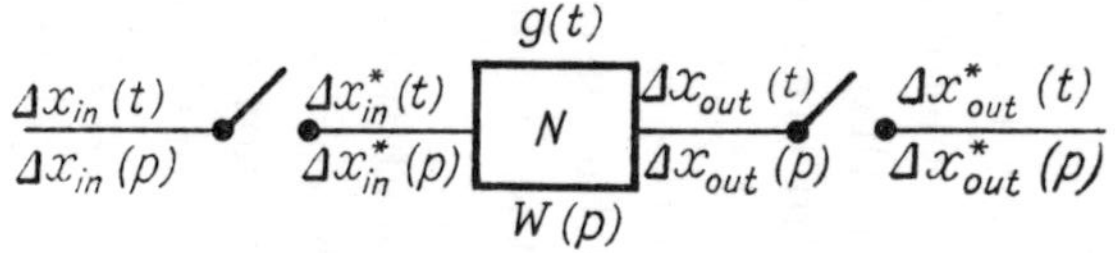	$W^*_1(p)\, \Delta x^*_{\text{out}}(p)$	$W_1(z)\, F(z)$
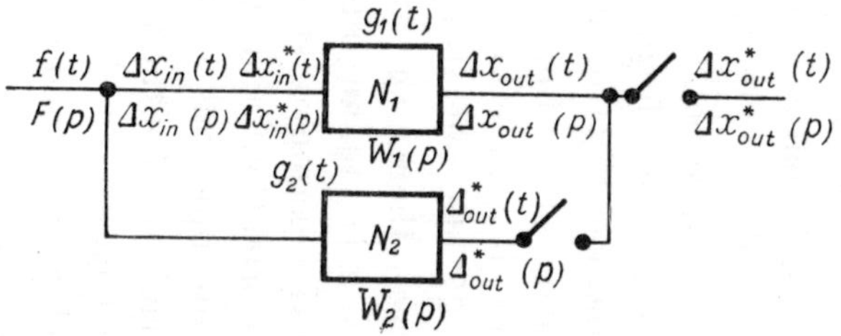	$\dfrac{W_1(p)\, F^*(p)}{1 + W_1 W_2(p)}$	$\dfrac{W_1(z)\, F(z)}{1 + W_1 W_2(z)}$

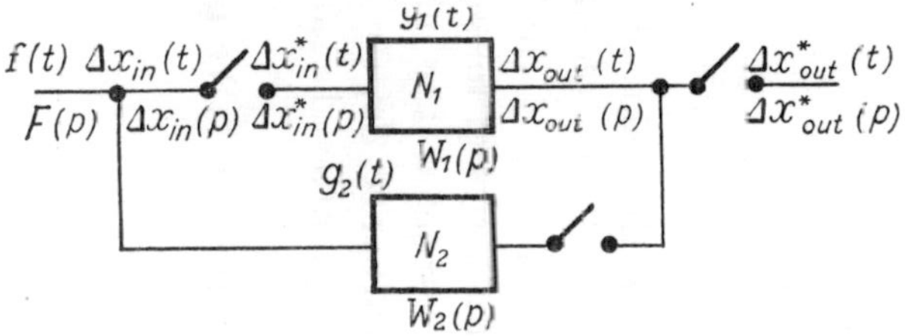	$\dfrac{W_1^*(p)\,F^*(p)}{1+W_1^*(p)\,W_2^*(p)}$	$\dfrac{W_1(z)\,F(z)}{1+W_1(z)\,W_2(z)}$
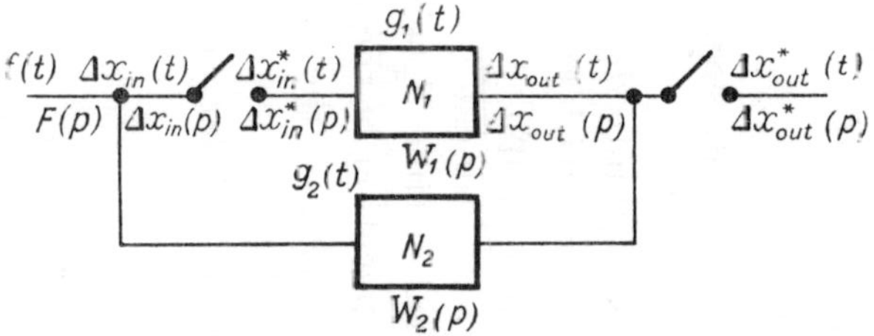	$W_1(p)\left[F(p) - \dfrac{W_2(p)\,F W_1^*(p)}{1+W_1 W_2^*(p)}\right]$	$\dfrac{F W_1(z)}{1+W_1 W_2(z)}$
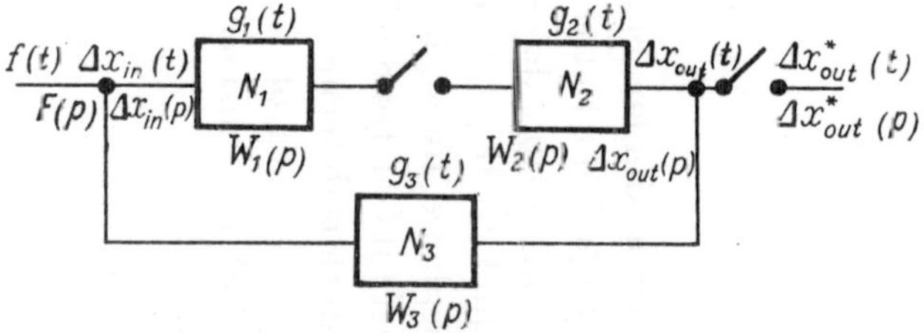	$\dfrac{W_2(p)\,F W_1^*(p)}{1+W_1 W_2 W_3^*(p)}$	$\dfrac{W_2(z)\,F W_1(z)}{1+W_1 W_2 W_3(z)}$

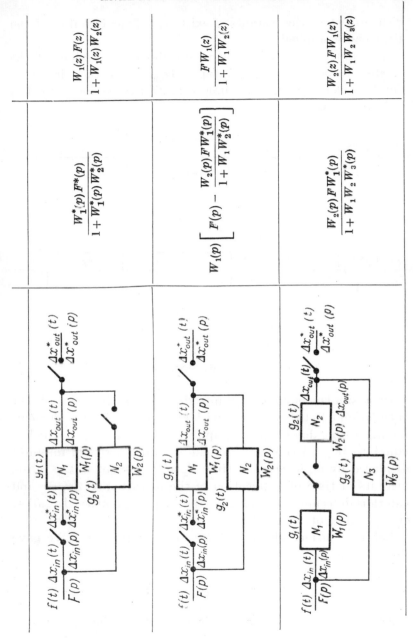

with respect to the instants of existence of the impulses of the disturbance applied

According to what has been said above, the values of the impulse response of the system, $\Delta x^*_{out}(t)$, of the circuit of Fig. 10,*a* at the instants of time 0, T, $2T$ can be determined as $L^{-1}\,[W^*(p)\Delta x^*_{in}(p)]$.

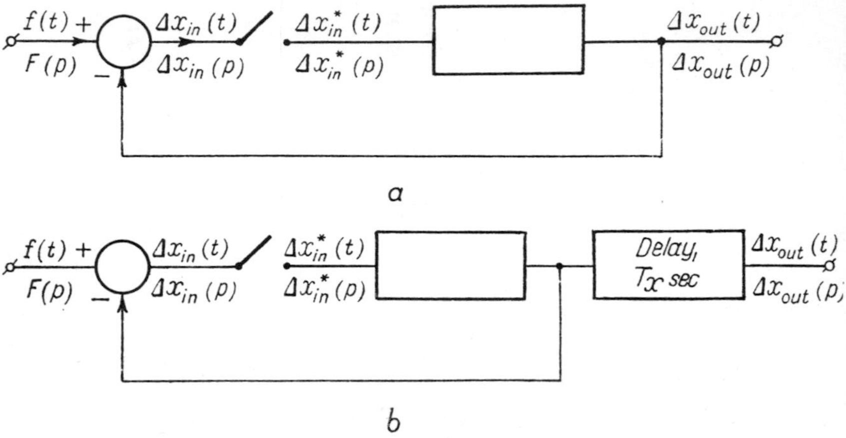

FIG. 10. To calculate stages with delay

In a similar manner, by introducing for the sake of our calculation a fictitious circuit with an additional delay element, having a time delay T_x, the impulse transfer factor of which is equal to $W_{Tx}(p)$ (Fig. 10), we can obtain a series of impulses displaced by an interval of time T_x with respect to the initial instants of time of application of the disturbance $\Delta x_{in}(t)$ and can thus determine the values of the output quantity $\Delta x^*_{out}(t)$ at the instants of time $kT+T_x$.

Let us consider the particular case $\Delta x_{in}(t) = e^{-at}$. We have for this case

$$W_{T_x}(p) = e^{-aT_x} + e^{-a(T+T_x)}\,e^{-pT} + e^{-a(2T+T_x)}\,e^{-2pT} + \ldots . \quad (5.44)$$

Taking the factor e^{-aT_x} outside brackets, replacing e^{pT} by z

and summing the series we obtain

$$W_{T_x}(z) = \frac{e^{-aT_x}z}{z-e^{-aT}}. \tag{5.45}$$

Corresponding expressions can be obtained in a similar manner for other functions also.

A short summary of such type of generalized z-transforms is given in Table 3.

TABLE 3.

TABLE OF MODIFIED z-TRANSFORMS

$W(z)$	$W_{T_x}(z)$
$\frac{z}{z-1}$	$\frac{z}{z-1}$
$\frac{Tz}{(z-1)^2}$	$\frac{T_x z}{z-1} + \frac{Tz}{(z-1)^2}$
$\frac{z}{z-e^{-aT}}$	$\frac{e^{-aT_x}z}{z-e^{-aT}}$

Example. We shall consider, as an example, Fig. 10,*b*. Let

$$W(p) = \frac{13.4}{p(p+10)} = 1.34\left(\frac{1}{p} - \frac{1}{p+10}\right). \tag{5.46}$$

Then, according to Table 1, we have for $T = 0.1$

$$W^*(p) = W(z) = 1.34\left(\frac{z}{z-1} - \frac{z}{z-e^{-1}}\right) = \frac{0.846\,z}{z^2-1.368z+0.368}. \tag{5.47}$$

The value of the input signal $\Delta x_{\text{in}}(z)$ is expressed in terms of the value of the external disturbance $F(z)$ and the transfer factor $W(z)$ in the following manner†

$$\Delta x_{\text{in}}(z) = \frac{F(z)}{1+W(z)} = \frac{z^2-0.368z}{z^2-0.522z+0.368}. \tag{5.48}$$

We shall obtain, correspondingly, for the transform of the input quantity $L[\Delta x^*_{\text{out}}(t)] = \Delta x_{\text{out}}(z)$, when $f(t)$ is a unit step,

$$\Delta x_{\text{out}}(z) = L[\Delta x^*_{\text{out}}(t)] = [1(t)]^* \frac{W(z)}{1+W(z)} = \frac{z}{z-1}\,\frac{0.846z}{z^2-0.522z+0.368}, \tag{5.49}$$

By dividing the numerator by the denominator and restricting ourselves to the first four terms we obtain

$$\Delta x_{\text{out}}(z) = \frac{0.846}{z} + \frac{1.29}{z^2} + \frac{1.20}{z^3} + \frac{1.01}{z^4} + \dots \tag{5.50}$$

We shall proceed now to the determination of intermediate values by means of the modified z-transform. If $T_x = 0.02$ sec (i.e. $0.2T$, where T is the operating period of the pulser), then, according to (5.40) and (5.42) and also from the Table 3, we have

$$W_{0.02}(z) = 1.34\left(\frac{z}{z-1} - \frac{e^{-0.2}z}{z-e^{-1}}\right) = \frac{0.242z^2+0.605z}{(z-1)\,(z-0.368)}, \tag{5.51}$$

and correspondingly

$$[\Delta x_{\text{out}}(z)]_{0.02} = \frac{0.242z^3+0.605z^2}{z^3-1.522z^2+0.890z-0.368}. \tag{5.52}$$

By dividing the numerator by the denominator and by restricting ourselves to the first four terms, we obtain

$$[\Delta x_{\text{out}}(z)]_{0.02} = 0.242 + \frac{0.973}{z} + \frac{1.265}{z^2} + \frac{1.149}{z^3} + \dots \tag{5.53}$$

† $\Delta x_{\text{in}} = F(z) - \Delta x_{\text{out}}$ or $\Delta x^*_{\text{in}}(p) = F^*(p) - \Delta x^*_{\text{out}}(p)$, and, by bearing in mind that $\Delta x^*_{\text{out}}(p) = W(p)\ \Delta x^*_{\text{in}}(p)$, we obtain $\Delta x_{\text{in}}(p) = F^*(p)/[1+W^*(p)]$, whence, after passing to the z-transforms, we obtain (5.48).

In a similar manner we can also carry out the calculation for the case $T_x = 0.06$ sec. We have for this case

$$[W(z)_{0,06} = 1.34\left[\frac{z}{z-1} - \frac{e^{-0.6}z}{z-e^{-1}}\right] = \frac{0.605z^2+0.243z}{(z-1)(z-0.368)}. \quad (5.54)$$

Correspondingly $[\Delta x_{\text{out}}]_{00,6}$ will be equal to

$$[\Delta x_{\text{out}}]_{0.06} = \frac{0.605z^3+0.243z^2}{z^3-1.522z^2+0.890z-0.368}. \quad (5.55)$$

After expanding in a series of negative powers of z, we obtain.

$$[\Delta x_{\text{out}}]_{0.06} = 0.605+\frac{1.165}{z}+\frac{1.237}{z^2}+\frac{1.063}{z^3}+\ldots \quad [(5.56)$$

7. The passage through a pulse circuit of a signal displaced in time with respect to the instants of application of the impulses

Let us consider the application of the z-transformation to impulse systems possessing a delay. If a time function is retarded by a time τ, the ordinary Laplace transform of the output function possessing the indicated delay is equal to

$$e^{-p\tau}/p+a.$$

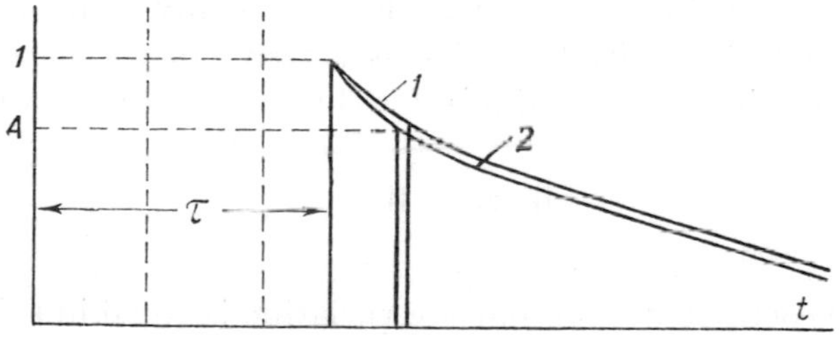

FIG. 11. To calculate the shift of the signal with respect to the instants of application of impulses: 1. the original function; 2. the function after the pulser

When we pass to the z-transform of such a function we must take into account the fact that, in the general case, when τ is not an integral multiple of the period of the impulses, the first impulse can have an amplitude smaller than unity (if we take as unity the amplitude of the original impulse).

This is illustrated in Fig. 11.

If $(m-1)T < \tau < mT$, no impulse whatever is present at the output of the system between the instant $t = 0$ and the instant $t = mT$, and only at the instant of time mT does an impulse appear at the output of the system. This impulse has an amplitude equal to A where $A < 1$, the value of A depending on the interval between the instant of time τ and the instant of time mT.

Since in an impulse system the values of the function are only considered at the instants of time $0, T, 2T, \ldots, mT$, then for the z-transform of the function e^{-aT} occurring with a delay τ, we consider as the initial time function the function

$$W(z) = W_0(z)\frac{1}{z^m}e^{-a(mT-\tau)}. \tag{5.57}$$

It is assumed here that τ is comprised between the intervals of time $(m-1)T$ and mT, and $W_0(z)$ is the z-transform of the initial exponential function in the absence of delay, the factor z^{-m} corresponds to a delay by mT sec and the exponential function is a factor indicating by how many times the initial value of the amplitude varies as a result of the delay.

We obtain correspondingly for the z-transform of a unit step

$$W(z) = W_0(z)\frac{1}{z^m}, \tag{5.58}$$

i.e. the coefficient of amplitude variation is equal in this case to unity.

In the general case of an arbitrary function $f(t)$ the coefficient of amplitude variation is equal to $f[a(mT-\tau)]/f(\tau)$. It is difficult to give a general rule for the determination of the z-transform of the system function for the general case of an element having a pure delay connected in series with a circuit having a transfer factor $W(p)$.

The difficulties arising here are determined by the fact that the coefficient of amplitude variation changes as the impulse passes from one element of the circuit to another.

The only known general technique consists in expanding $W(p)$ in elementary fractions, multiplying each term by $e^{-p\tau}$ and finding the corresponding z-transform.

8. Correspondence theorem for z-transforms

In concluding this part of our exposition we shall derive for z-transforms the initial and final value theorem, which is analogous to a known theorem of operational calculus.

Let the analytical expression for the z-transform of a certain function be equal to $\Delta x_{out}(z)$. By expanding $\Delta x_{out}(z)$ in elementary fractions we obtain

$$\Delta x_{out}(z) = \frac{A_0 z}{z-1} + \frac{A_1 z}{z-e^{-a_1 T}} + \frac{A_2 z}{z-e^{-a_2 T}} + \dots \quad (5.59)$$

After passing to the time domain we obtain

$$\Delta x_{out}(t) = A_0 + A_1 e^{-a_1 T} + A_2 e^{-a_2 T} + \dots \quad (5.60)$$

If $\Delta x_{out}(p)$ has no poles in the right-hand half of the p-plane or on the imaginary axis, all the terms in (5.60) will tend to zero as $t \to \infty$ except the term containing A_0. Hence, by bearing in mind that as $p \to 0$, $z \to 1$, we obtain from (5.54) for the z-transforms

$$\lim_{z\to 1} \frac{(z-1)\Delta x_{out}(z)}{z} = A_0 = \lim_{t\to\infty} \Delta x_{out}(t) = \lim_{z\to 1}(1-z^{-1})\Delta x_{out}(z). \quad (5.61)$$

The limit value of $\Delta x_{out}(t)$ as $t \to 0$ can be found from the expansion of $\Delta x_{out}(z)$ in a series of powers of z^{-1}, By carrying out the expansion indicated we obtain

$$\Delta x_{out}(z) = B_0 + B_1 z^{-1} + B_2 z^{-2}, \quad (5.62)$$

where B_0 is the value of $\Delta x_{out}(t)$ for $t = 0$ and B_1 is the value of $\Delta x_{out}(t)$ for $t = T$, etc.

The quantity B_0 can be found from the expression

$$\lim \Delta x_{out}(z) = \lim_{t\to 0} \Delta x_{out}(t) = B_0. \qquad (5.63)$$

If the initial value of $\Delta x_{out}(t)$ is equal to zero, we can find in a similar manner the value of $\Delta x_{out}(t)$ for $t = T$, i.e. the coefficient B_1. We have in this case

$$\lim_{z\to\infty} z\Delta x_{out}(z) = \Delta x_{out}(t)_{t\to T} = B_1. \qquad (5.64)$$

9. Functions that begin with the *k*-th impulse and functions having *k* additional impulses

Let us consider a function of the form

$$f(t+kT)1^*(t) = f_1^*(t) = \sum_{n=0}^{\infty} \{f[(n+k)T]1(t-nT) -$$
$$-f[(n+k)T]\,1(t-nT-\Delta)\}. \qquad (5.65)$$

The function $f_1^*(t)$ differs from the function $f^*(t)$ in that all impulses of the function $f_1^*(t)$ precede the corresponding impulses of the function $f^*(t)$ by an interval of time kT; in addition, the function $f_1^*(t)$ does not contain the first $(k-1)$ impulses of the function $f^*(t)$ (Fig. 12,*a*).

By taking the Laplace transform of both sides of (5.65) we can write for the function $f_1^*(t)$

$$L[f_1^*(t) = \sum_{n=\infty}^{\infty} f[(n+k)T]e^{-npT}. \qquad (5.66)$$

By introducing the notation $n+k = n_1$ we can rewrite (5.66) in the form

$$L[f_1^*(t)] = \sum_{n_1=k}^{\infty} f(n_1T)e^{-(n_1-k)pT} =$$

$$= e^{pkT}\left[\sum_{n_1=0}^{\infty} e^{-n_1pT} f(n_1T) - \sum_{n_1=0}^{k-1} e^{-n_1pT} f(n_1T)\right]. \qquad (5.67)$$

Bearing in mind that the result of the summation does not depend upon the notation of the variable, we obtain, after replacing n_1 by n in (5.67),

$$L[f_1^*(t)] = e^{pkT}\left[F^*(p) - \sum_{n_1=0}^{k-1} e^{-n_1pT} f(n_1T)\right]. \qquad (5.68)$$

We have, in a similar manner, for a function $f_2^*(t)$ delayed with respect to the function $f^*(t)$ by a time kT and having k

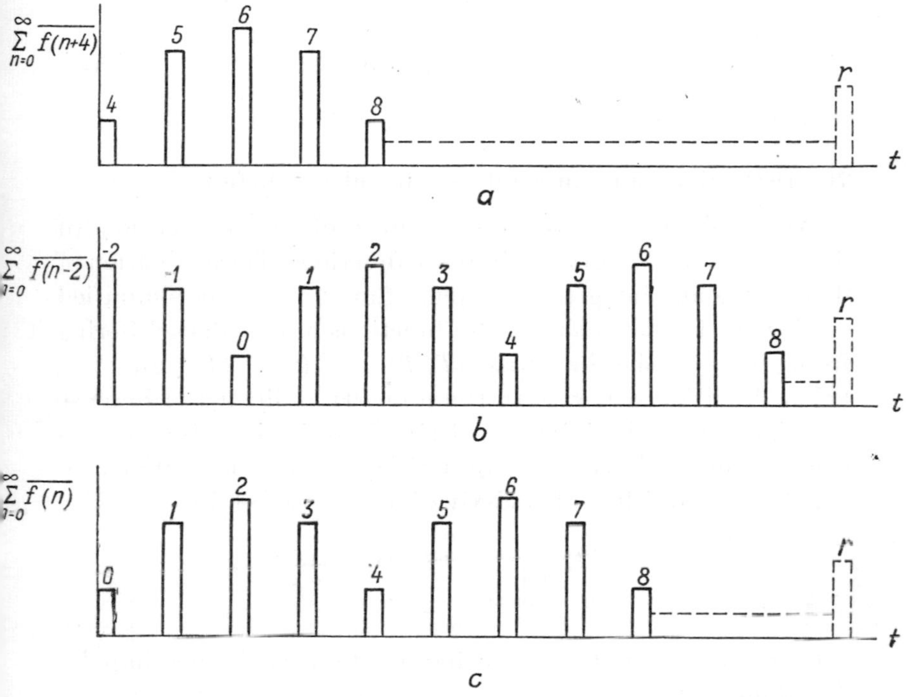

FIG. 12. To determine the derivatives of impulse functions

additional impulses (Fig. 12,*b*)

$$L[f_2^*(t)] = \sum_{n=0}^{\infty} f[(n-k)T]e^{-npT}. \qquad (5.69)$$

By introducing the notation $n-k = n_1$ we obtain

$$L[f_2^*(t)] = \sum_{n_1=-k}^{\infty} f(n_1 T)e^{-(n_1+k)pT} =$$

$$= e^{-pkT}\left[\sum_{n_1=0}^{\infty} f(n_1 T)e^{-n_1 pT} - \sum_{n_1=-k}^{-1} f(n_1 T)e^{-n_1 pT}\right] =$$

$$= e^{-pkT}\left[F^*(p) - \sum_{n_1=-k}^{-1} f(n_1 T)e^{-n_1 pT}\right]. \qquad (5.70)$$

For the sake of comparison, the function $\sum_{n=0}^{\infty} f(n)$ is shown in Fig. 12,*c*.

10. Derivatives and integrals of impulse functions

We shall examine certain features of the evaluation of derivatives and integrals of impulse functions. The evaluation of derivatives and integrals of impulse functions can be simplified in view of the fact that impulse functions have values differing from zero in the intervals $(T, T+\Delta)$, $(2T, 2T+\Delta)$, ..., $(kT, kT+\Delta)$ only. Owing to the property indicated of impulse functions, the obtaining of derivatives in impulse circuits can be replaced by the evaluation of suitable differences.

By the definition of a derivative, we can write

$$\frac{df(t)}{dt} = \lim_{\Delta t \to 0} \frac{f(t+\Delta t) - f(t)}{\Delta t}. \qquad (5.71)$$

Correspondingly the following relation holds for impulse functions

$$\frac{df^*(t)}{dt} = \frac{\Delta f^*(t)}{\Delta t} = \frac{f(t+T)1^*(t) - f(t)1^*(t)}{T} =$$

$$= \frac{1}{T}\sum_{n=0}^{\infty} \{f[(n+1)T]1(t-nT) - f[(n+1)T]\cdot 1(t-nT-\Delta) -$$

$$- f(nT)1(t-nT) + f(nT)1(t-nT-\Delta)\}. \qquad (5.72)$$

If we denote the impulse occurring at the instant of time T by $\overline{f(nT)}$, expression (5.72) can be written briefly in the form

$$\frac{df^*(t)}{dt} = \frac{1}{T} \sum_{n=0}^{\infty} \{\overline{f[n+1)T]} - \overline{f(nT)}\},$$

where

$$\overline{f[(n+k)T]} = f[(n+k)T]1(t-nT) - f(n+k)1(t-nT-\Delta). \quad (5.73)$$

We can find in a similar manner the second derivative of an impulse function

$$\frac{d^2f^*(t)}{dt^2} = \frac{\Delta f(t+T)1^*(t) - \Delta f(t)1^*(t)}{T^2} =$$

$$= \frac{1}{T^2} \sum_{n=0}^{\infty} \{f[(n+2)T]1(t-nT) - f[(n+2)T]1(t-nT-\Delta) -$$
$$- f[(n+1)T]1(t-nT) + f[(n+1)T]1(t-nT-\Delta) - f[(n+$$
$$+1)T]1(t-nT) + f[(n+1)T]1(t-nT-\Delta) + f(nT)1(t-$$
$$-nT) - f(nT)1(t-nT-\Delta)\} = \frac{1}{T^2} \sum_{n=0}^{\infty} \{[f(n+2)T]1(t-nT) -$$
$$- f[(n+2)T]1(t-nT-\Delta) - 2f[(n+1)T]1(t-nT) + 2f[(n+$$
$$+1)]1(t-nT) + f(nT)1(t-nT) - f(nT)1(t-nT-\Delta)\}. \quad (5.74)$$

If we introduce the notation

$$\overline{f[(n+k)T]} = f[(n+k)T]1[t-nT] - f[(n+k)T]1[t-(n+$$
$$+k)T-\Delta], \quad (5.75)$$

the expression (5.24) can be rewritten in the form

$$\frac{d^{2*}f(t)}{dt^2} = \frac{1}{T^2} \sum_{n=0}^{\infty} \{\overline{f[(n+2)T]} - 2\overline{f[(n+1)T]} + \overline{f(nT)}\}. \quad (5.76)$$

We can obtain in a similar manner expressions for the third and higher derivatives. By analogy with (5.74) we can write for the third derivative

$$\frac{d^3f^*(t)}{dt^3} = \frac{\Delta^2 f(t+T)1^*(t) - \Delta^2 f(t)1^*(t)}{T^3}. \quad (5.77)$$

If we write the expressions for the second derivatives occurring in the numerator of (5.77) in the abbreviated form according to (5.75), we obtain, after transformations,

$$\frac{d^3 f^*(t)}{dt^3} = \frac{1}{T^3} \sum_{n=0}^{\infty} \{\overline{[f(n+3)T]} - 3\overline{f[(n+2)T]} + \overline{+3f[(n+1)T]} - \overline{f(nT)}\}. \tag{5.78}$$

By comparing the expressions obtained for the first three derivatives it can easily be seen that the coefficients of the terms in curled brackets are determined by the same rule that determines the binomial coefficients. We have, accordingly, for the k-th derivative

$$\frac{d^{(k)} f^*(t)}{dt^{(k)}} = \frac{1}{T^k} \sum_{\nu=0}^{k} \sum_{n=0}^{\infty} (-1)^\nu C_\nu^k \overline{f(n+k-\nu)} = \sum_{\nu=0}^{k} \sum_{n=0}^{\infty} (-1)^\nu \frac{k!}{\nu!\,(k-\nu)!} f(n+k-\nu). \tag{5.79}$$

In the preceding derivation, to determine the differences, we have subtracted the value of the n-th impulse from the value of the $(n+1)$-th impulse. In a similar manner, we could have determined the differences by subtracting the value of the $(n-1)$-th impulse from the n-th one. The corresponding expressions are referred to as ascending differences. Expressions for the ascending differences can be obtained from those shown above by replacing n by $(n-1)$. Thus, for example, the first ascending difference will be written in the form

$$\Delta f^*(t) = \sum_{n=0}^{\infty} \{f(nT)1(t-nT) - f(nT)1(t-nT-\Delta) - f[(n-1)T]1(t-nT) + f[(n-1)T]1(t-nT-\Delta). \tag{5.80}$$

The evaluation of integrals of impulse functions can be replaced by the evaluation of the corresponding sums.

We have, in fact, by definition

$$\int f(t)dt = \lim_{\Delta t \to 0} \sum_{k=0}^{\infty} f(tnT\,)\Delta t. \tag{5.81}$$

We can write for impulse circuits, directly,

$$\int f^*(t)dt = \sum_{n=0}^{n-1} \overline{f(nT)\Delta} = \Delta \sum_{n=0}^{n-1} \overline{f(nT)}, \tag{5.82}$$

where Δ is the width of an impulse; i.e. in impulse circuits the sum occurring in the right-hand side of (5.82) has the role of the integral.

As can be seen from the formulae (5.72)–(5.82), the differences $\Delta f(nT)$ and the sums $\sum_{k=0}^{n} f(nT)$ of impulse functions are also impulse functions. Thus the differences are different from zero at instants of time only when the initial impulse function $f^*(t)$ itself is different from zero, while the sums vary discontinuously for $t = nT$, where n is an integer.

The Laplace transforms and the z-transforms of differences (and of the corresponding derivatives) $\Delta^{(k)} f(nT)$ can be obtained in the same manner as for the initial function on the basis of the formulae (5.2), (5.3) and (5.6)

Thus, for example, we obtain for the first derivative (see § 9)

$$L\left[\frac{df^*(t)}{dt}\right] = \frac{1}{T} L \sum_{n=0}^{\infty} \{f[(n+1)T]1(t-nT) -$$

$$-f[(n+1)T]1(t-nT-\Delta) - f(nT)1(t-nT) + f(nT)1(t-$$

$$-nT-\Delta)\} = \frac{V(p)}{T}\{F^*(p)e^{-pT} - f(0)e^{-pT} - F^*(p)\} =$$

$$= \frac{V(p)}{T}\{F^*(p)\,(e^{-pT}-1) - f(0)e^{-pT}\}. \tag{5.83}$$

We can also obtain, in a similar manner, the Laplace transforms of derivatives of higher orders. The expression for the Laplace transform of the k-th derivative will have the following form

$$L\left[\frac{df^*(t)}{dt}\right] = \frac{e^{pT}}{e^{-pT}-1} \sum_{\nu=0}^{k-1} \frac{\Delta^{\nu} f(0)}{(e^{-pT}-1)^{\nu}} + \frac{1}{(e^{b}-1)^{k}} L\{\Delta^{k} f^*(t)\}. \tag{5.84}$$

11. The choice of the parameters of pulse (digital) correcting equipment

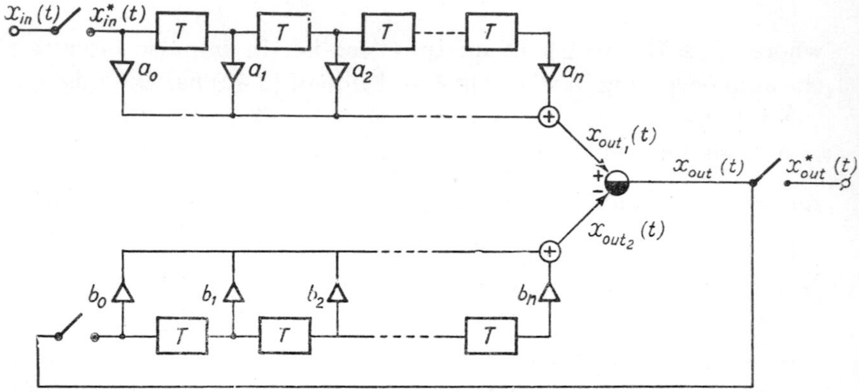

FIG. 13. Block diagram of a universal impulse correcting stage: T – impulse-delay element; a and b – impulse-weighting coefficients

The method for designing an automatic-control pulse system with an assigned frequency characteristic of the transfer factor, based on the use of pulse and digital techniques, can be clarified by means of Fig. 13 and Fig. 14.

In Fig. 13 is shown a universal pulse digital correcting element. In Fig. 14 is shown one of the possible methods of connecting an impulse element.

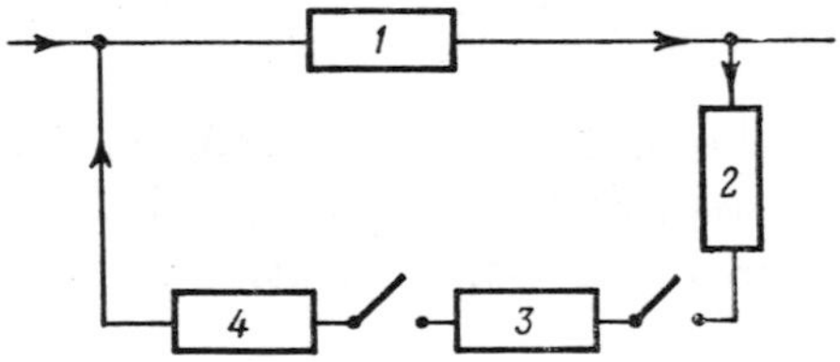

FIG. 14. A method of connecting an impulse correcting stage: 1 – the stage to be controlled; 2 – measuring control element; 3 – correcting (digital) stage of the controller; 4 – actuating stage of the controller

A universal pulse correcting element consists of two equal units. At the input of the first unit is applied the input signal. At the input of the second unit is applied the output signal.

A pulser at the input of the first unit interrupts, at equal intervals of time, the error signal (Fig. 14). The signal, arriving at the input of the first unit, propagates along a delay line which can be realised either in the form of a physical line or in the form of suitable digital equipment. The signal, arriving at the input of the unit, propagates along the line with a finite speed, as a result of which at each instant of time at different points of the line there will be voltages proportional to impulses that have passed at previous instants of time. At the same time the impulses are deformed, but, as a result of the pulse operation of the entire equipment, the deformation of the impulses cannot on the whole exert any influence on the operation of the equipment. At the junction points of the delay line impulses occur after an interval of time T. If the delay line of the first unit has k junction points, then at each instant of time the voltage at the output of the first unit will be proportional respectively to the incoming impulse and to $k-1$ previous impulses. The voltage of the junction points of the delay line is measured at the output of amplifiers having gains suitably chosen. The outputs of the amplifiers are mixed and form the output signal of the first unit. Thus the impulse at the output of the first unit represents at any instant of time a linear combination of the last value of the input impulse and of the $(k-1)$ values preceding it

$$\begin{aligned}\overline{x_{\text{out}_1}(nT)} &= \overline{a_0 x_{\text{in}_1}(nT)} + \overline{a_1 x_{\text{in}_1}[(n-1)T]} + \ldots + \\ &+ \overline{a_{k-1} x_{\text{in}_1}[(n-k+1)T]} + \overline{a_k x_{\text{in}_1}[(n-k)T]}. \end{aligned} \tag{5.85}$$

In a similar manner the output impulse of the second unit is equal, at the instant of time nT, to

$$\begin{aligned}\overline{x_{\text{out}_2}(nT)} &= \overline{b_0 x_{\text{out}}(nT)} + \overline{b_1 x_{\text{out}}[(n-1)T]} + \ldots + \\ &+ b_m x_{\text{out}}[(n-m)T]. \end{aligned} \tag{5.86}$$

We obtain for the signal at the output of the first unit

$$x^*_{\text{out}_1}(t) = \sum_{n=0}^{\infty} \overline{x_{\text{out}_1}(nT)} = a_0 \sum_{n=0}^{\infty} \overline{x_{\text{in}_1}(nT)} +$$

$$+ a_1 \sum_{n=0}^{\infty} \overline{x_{\text{in}_1}[(n-1)T]} + \ldots + a_{k-1} \sum_{n=0}^{\infty} \overline{x_{\text{in}_1}[(n-k)T]}. \qquad (5.87)$$

In a similar manner the output signal of the second unit is equal to

$$x^*_{\text{out}_2}(t) = \sum_{n=0}^{\infty} \overline{x_{\text{out}}[nT]} = b_0 \sum_{n=0}^{\infty} \overline{x_{\text{out}}[nT]} +$$

$$+ b_1 \sum_{n=0}^{\infty} \overline{x_{\text{out}}[(n-1)T]} + \ldots + b_{n-1} \sum_{n=0}^{\infty} \overline{x_{\text{out}}[(n-m)T]}. \qquad (5.88)$$

By passing in (5.87) and (5.88) to the Laplace transforms and taking into account that $\sum_{n=0}^{\infty} \overline{f[(n-1)T]} = f^*(t-T)$ and that, accordingly, $L \sum_{n=0}^{\infty} \overline{f[(n-1)T]} = e^{-pT} L[f^*(t)]$, we obtain the following expressions

$$L[x^*_{\text{out}_1}(t)] = a_0 L[x^*_{\text{in}_1}(t)] + a_1 e^{-pT} L[x^*_{\text{in}_1}(t)] +$$

$$+ \ldots + a_k e^{-kpT} L[x^*_{\text{in}_1}(t)] = \sum_{n=0}^{\infty} a_n e^{-npT} L[x^*_{\text{in}_1}(t)] \qquad (5.89)$$

and, in a similar manner,

$$L[x^*_{\text{out}_2}(t)] = \sum_{m=0}^{\infty} b_m e^{-mpT} \cdot L[x^*_{\text{out}}(t)]. \qquad (5.90)$$

The resulting signal at the output of the two units is equal to

$$\sum_{n=0}^{\infty} \overline{x_{\text{out}}(nT)} = \sum_{n=0}^{\infty} \overline{x_{\text{out}_1}(nT)} - \sum_{n=0}^{\infty} x_{\text{out}_2}(nT). \qquad (5.91)$$

Taking the transforms of both sides of (5.91) and taking into account (5.89) and (5.90)

$$L[x^*_{\text{out}}(t)] = L[x^*_{\text{in}_1}(t)] \sum_{n=0}^{n} a_n e^{-npT} -$$

$$- L[x^*_{\text{out}}(t)] \sum_{m=0}^{m} b_m e^{-mpT}. \qquad (5.92)$$

Let us find the transfer factor of the impulse element of Fig. 13. Let us denote e^{pT} by Z and the wanted transfer factor by $W(Z)$. Then we can write, by definition of transfer factor†

$$W(Z) = \sum_{n=0}^{n} a_n Z^{-n} : \sum_{m=0}^{m} c_m Z^{-m}. \tag{5.93}$$

The coefficients a_n, b_m and c_m are called the weighting coefficients.

The synthesis of an automatic-control pulse (or digital) system reduces to the choice of the parameters of the digital (or pulse) correcting element, i.e. reduces to the determination of the values of n and m and of the values of the weighting coefficients a and c.

The synthesis of an automatic-control pulse (or digital) system is carried out in the following manner: (1) the z-transform of the disturbance applied is evaluated, (2) having assigned the general form of the transfer factor of the pulse correcting element $K(z) = P(z)/Q(z)$, i.e. having assigned the degree of $P(z)$ and $Q(z)$ (the values of m and n), we determine the expression of the overall transfer factor of the pulse controller with the feedback loop closed; (3) proceeding from the operating conditions of the system (the assigned duration of the transient, the minimum mean-square error etc.) we determine $\Delta x_{\text{out}}(t)$ and then $\Delta x_{\text{out}}(z)$; (4) proceeding from the relation

$$\Delta x_{\text{out}}(z) = W(z)F(z). \tag{5.94}$$

we determine the overall transfer factor $W(z)$ of the pulsed (or digital) controller and, at the same time, by equating the coefficients of equal powers of z, we determine the values of the coefficients a and b.

The determination of the general form of the transfer factor of the correcting element, i.e. the determination of the highest power of z occurring in the numerator and denominator of

† We have in (5.93), according to (5.92): $c_m = b_m$ for $m \neq 0$ and $c_0 = b_0 + 1$.

$K(z)$, is carried out proceeding from the form of the transfer factor of the main part of the system in such a manner that the number of zeros and poles of the correcting element may ensure optimum behaviour of the transient. In this connection a necessary condition is the physical realizability of the correcting element and the absence, in the expression for its transfer factor, of zeros cancelling with poles of the transfer factor of the non-correcting part of the system situated in the left-hand half-plane.

The first condition is connected with satisfying the requirement of causality, i.e. the requirement of absence, in the expression for $K(z)$, of positive powers of z. The second condition is determined by the requirement of retaining the stability of the system in the presence of unforeseen variations of the parameters (i.e. it is connected with the requirement of "coarseness" of the system). If, in fact, owing to the introduction of artificial zeros by means of the correcting equipment we cancel poles situated in the right-hand half-plane, then, in the presence of a small variation of the parameters, this cancelling-out will no longer occur and accordingly the system becomes unstable.[17]

The problems of the synthesis of pulse automatic-control systems have been sufficiently clarified in the literature as far as systems with constant parameters are concerned. The synthesis of pulse systems with variable parameters is associated with the difficulty of determining the z-transform of the transfer factors of elements having variable parameters.

The method outlined above enables us to determine the z-transforms of systems with periodically varying parameters.

In the general case of systems with arbitrarily varying parameters, the operating modes of which are of interest or are assigned over an assigned finite interval of time, the general solution of the problem can be obtained by combining the results obtained for systems with periodically varying parameters with the Fourier-series method (i.e. the method of reduction to steady-state operating modes).

In connection with the use of the results shown in Chapters II and III, we must bear in mind that in pulse or digital systems, by the very nature of their operation, all system elements work under operating conditions characterized by the fact that step-wise or impulse voltages are applied to them. This fact must be taken into account in evaluating the z-transform, since, as has been indicated, in systems with variable parameters the z-transform cannot be represented in the form of the product of the transform of the disturbance applied times a transfer factor. Here, we can use, for example, the formulae (3.24) and (3.25) or formulae similar to them. It proves convenient here, in passing to the z-transforms, to express all trigonometric functions of the operator p occurring in the L-transform in terms of $\cot(p-a)$, and $\cot(p-a)$ in terms of z.

CHAPTER VI

THE STABILITY OF CIRCUITS WITH VARIABLE PARAMETERS AND THE STABILITY OF PERIODIC MODES OF OPERATION IN NON-LINEAR CIRCUITS

1. General considerations

Electrical circuits with variable parameters are active circuits. Energy from without can be introduced in the system at the expense of the parameter variation. Owing to this, in contrast to systems with constant parameters, free oscillations can be undamped in this case and, under certain conditions, can grow, i.e. self-excitation arises. Similar phenomena can also occur in non-linear circuits when periodic disturbances are applied to them; in these, however, in contrast to linear circuits, the amplitude of the oscillations arising is limited by the non-linearity. When feedback amplifiers are present in a circuit, as is the case in automatic-control circuits, the probability of undamped oscillations arising increases considerably.

In view of this, feedback circuits comprising variable parameters or oscillatory non-linear elements can prove unstable or liable to unstable oscillations, even when the feedback loops are open. Therefore, in investigating the stability of automatic-control systems comprising elements with variable parameters or oscillatory non-linear elements, we need first of all to investigate the stability of the open-loop system and the possibility of the existence in it of periodic and quasi-periodic modes of operation.

The investigation of the stability of circuits comprising periodically varying parameters and of the stability of periodic modes of operation in circuits comprising oscillatory non-linear elements reduces to investigating the stability of the solutions of a system of linear differential equations with periodically varying parameters. We can use for such an investigation Mikhailov's frequency criterion, but we need to examine in detail certain features of its application to systems of equations with periodic parameters, features connected with the properties of these systems of equations.

Here, for the cases investigated, two approaches are possible: (1) an approximate method based on assuming the presence of an ideal filter, only the lower frequencies of the spectrum in the system of the ideal filter being taken into account, (2) the exact method allowing for all frequencies.[4,6]

We shall deal at first with the approximate method for investigating the stability of systems with variable parameters. For the sake of completeness, we shall discuss it in application to the analysis of the stability of periodic modes of operation in non-linear circuits.

2. Approximate method for investigating of the stability of periodic modes of operation

(a) The equation of small deviations, and reduction of the problem to investigating a characteristic equation of infinite degree

Let us consider an automatic control system consisting of an arbitrary linear part and of a non-linear feedback. Let the equations of the process be

$$D(p)X = -K(p)Y;$$
$$Y = F(X, X', X''), \tag{6.1}$$

where $p = d/dt$, and D and K are polynomials (the degree of K being lower than that of D) with constant coefficients.

It is assumed that $|K(j\omega)/D(j\omega)| = 0$ for $\omega > \omega_{\text{cut}}$, i. e. that ω_{cut} is the upper boundary of the transmission band of the linear filter. The function $F(X)$ is assumed to be odd, but this restriction is introduced for the sake of concreteness and can be easily removed.

In order to determine the stability we shall pass to the increments by making in (6.1) the following substitutions

$$X = \overline{X(t)}+x; \quad X' = \overline{X'(t)}+x'; \quad X'' = \overline{X''(t)}+x''. \tag{6.2}$$

By substituting (6.2) in (6.1) we find

$$D(p)\overline{X(t)}+D(p)x = -K(p)F[\overline{X(t)}+x;\ \overline{X'(t)}+x';\ \overline{X''(t)}+x''].$$

By expanding the non-linear function in a power series with respect to x, x' and x'' for sufficiently small values of x, x' and x'', neglecting the non-linear terms of the expansion and taking into account that $X(t)$ satisfies the equation (6.1), we find

$$D(p)x+K(p)[A_x(t)x+A_{x'}(t)x'+A_{x''}(t)x''] = 0, \tag{6.3}$$

where

$$A_X(t)=\left[\frac{\partial F(X,X',X'')}{\partial X}\right]_{X=X(t)}; \quad A_{X'}(t)=\left[\frac{\partial F(X,X',X'')}{\partial X'}\right]_{X'=X'(t)};$$

$$A_{X''}(t)=\left[\frac{\partial F(X,X',X'')}{\partial X''}\right]_{X''=X''(t)}$$

are assigned functions of time, periodic with period Ω.

Let us represent the periodic functions (6.3) by their expansion in Fourier series†

$$A_x(t)= A_x+A_x m_{1x}\cos(\Omega t+\alpha_{1x})+A_x m_{2x}\cos(2\Omega t+\alpha_{2x})+\ldots$$

$$A_{x'}(t)= A_{x'}+A_{x'}m_{1x'}\cos(\Omega t+\alpha_{1x'})+A_{x'}m_{2x'}\cos(2\Omega t+\alpha_{2x'})+\ldots$$

$$\varDelta_{x''}(t)= A_{x''}+A_{x''}m_{1x''}\cos(\Omega t+\alpha_{1x''})+A_{x''}m_{2x''}\cos(2\Omega t+\alpha_{2x''}). \tag{6.4}$$

† The coefficients of the expansion of certain standard non-linearities are given in Table 4. This has been compiled by S. M. ZAIDEL' in connection with calculations carried out according to the method described.

In order that the investigated periodic mode of operation, determined by the equations (6.1), be stable, it is necessary and sufficient that the solution of the linear equation with periodic coefficients (6.3) be stable.

We shall seek the general solution of the differential equation with periodic coefficients (6.3) in the following form

$$x(t) = \mathrm{Re} \sum_{k=-\infty}^{\infty} X_K e^{\lambda_i + j(k\Omega t + \varphi_k)}, \tag{6.5}$$

where λ_i are characteristic numbers subject to determination, and X are the required amplitudes.

If we substitute (6.4) and (6.5) in (6.3), we obtain after simple transformations, for the simplest case $\partial F/\partial X' = \partial F/\partial X'' = 0$,

$$\begin{aligned} A_0 K(p) \Bigg[& \sum_{k=-\infty}^{\infty} X_k e^{[\lambda t + j(k\Omega t + \varphi_k)]} + \frac{m_1 e^{ja}}{2} \sum_{k=-\infty}^{\infty} X_k e^{\{\lambda t + j[(k+1)\Omega t + \varphi_k]\}} + \\ & + \frac{m_1 e^{-ja_1}}{2} \sum_{k=-\infty}^{\infty} X_k e^{\{\lambda t + j[(k-1)\Omega t + \varphi_k]\}} + \dots \\ & + \frac{m_r e^{ja_r}}{2} \sum_{k=-\infty}^{\infty} X_k e^{\{\lambda t + j[(k+r)\Omega t + \varphi_k]\}} + \\ & + \frac{m_r e^{-ja_r}}{2} \sum_{k=-\infty}^{\infty} X_k e^{\{\lambda t + j[(k-r)\Omega t + \varphi_k]\}} + \dots \Bigg] + \\ & + D(p) \sum_{k=-\infty}^{\infty} X_k e^{[\lambda t + j(k\Omega t + \varphi_k)]} = 0. \end{aligned} \tag{6.6}$$

By replacing k by $k+r$ in all sums and introducing the notation $\dot{X}_k = X_k e^{j\varphi k}$, we can rewrite (6.6) in the form

$$\begin{aligned} & [A_0 K(p) + D(p)] \sum_{k=-\infty}^{\infty} \dot{X}_k e^{(\lambda t + jk\Omega t)} + \\ & + \frac{1}{2} A_0 K(p) m_1 e^{ja_1} \sum_{k=-\infty}^{\infty} \dot{X}_{k-1} e^{(\lambda t + jk\Omega t)} + \dots \\ & \dots + \frac{1}{2} A_0 K(p) m_r e^{ja_r} \sum_{k=-\infty}^{\infty} \dot{X}_{k-r} e^{(\lambda t + jk\Omega t)} + \\ & + \frac{1}{2} A_0 K(p) m_r e^{-ja_r} \sum_{k=-\infty}^{\infty} X_{k+r} e^{[\lambda t + jk\Omega t]} + \dots = 0. \end{aligned} \tag{6.7}$$

If we equate to zero the complex amplitudes of equal frequencies, equation (6.7) is resolved into a system of an infinite number of equations, each of which contains an infinite number of components.

$$\{[A_0K(p)+D(p)]e^{(\lambda+jk\Omega)t}\}\dot{X}_k+\left[\frac{1}{2}A_0m_1e^{j\alpha_1}K(p)e^{(\lambda+jk\Omega)t}\right]\dot{X}_{k-1}+$$

$$+\left[\frac{1}{2}A_0m_1e^{-j\alpha_1}K(p)e^{(\lambda+jk\Omega)t}\right]\dot{X}_{k+1}+\ldots+$$

$$+\left[\frac{1}{2}A_0m_re^{j\alpha_r}K(p)e^{(\lambda+jk\Omega t)}\right]\dot{X}_{k-r}+$$

$$+\left[\frac{1}{2}A_0m_re^{-j\alpha_r}K(p)e^{(\lambda+jk\Omega t)}\right]\dot{X}_{k+r}+\ldots=0$$

$$(k=-\infty,\ldots,-1,\ 0,\ 1,\ldots,\infty). \tag{6.8}$$

By equating to zero the determinant of this infinite system of equations, we obtain a characteristic equation of infinite degree with respect to λ. Its roots are the values of λ required. In order that the investigated mode of operation be stable, it is necessary and sufficient that they all have a negative real part. In such a form, of course, the stability conditions are inapplicable in practice. So far, however, we have not yet made use of the filter conditions, which we can now use.

(b) The filter conditions and the reduction of the degree of the characteristic equation

If we bear in mind that, as a result of the presence of a finite cut-off frequency, the complex amplitudes of the components the frequency of which exceeds the cut-off frequency are equal to zero, we can pass from an infinite system of equations to a finite system of equations. If the cut-off frequency is equal to ω_{cut}, the complex amplitudes corresponding to values of k that satisfy the condition

$$(Im\lambda+k\Omega)\geqslant\omega_{cut}, \tag{6.9}$$

will be identically equal to zero.

Bearing in mind that the quantities λ are unknown, we can replace the condition (6.9) by the approximate condition

$$k\Omega \geqslant \omega_{\text{cut}}, \tag{6.10}$$

from which the limiting value of k, equal to k_{lim}, corresponding to which the complex amplitude is equal to zero, will be determined as

$$k_{\text{lim}} \geqslant \frac{\omega_{\text{cut}}}{\Omega}. \tag{6.11}$$

For example, if $\omega_{\text{cut}} = 2\Omega$, we obtain, instead of the infinite system of equations (6.8), a finite system of five equations.

By denoting the coefficient of a diagonal term (of the complex amplitude $\dot{X}_{kk}$) by a_k, and the non-diagonal coefficient at the intersection of the k-th row with the $(k+r)$-th column by $a_{k,\,k+r}$, and assuming $\omega_{\text{cut}} = 2\Omega$, we obtain from (6.8) a finite system of equations which can be written in the following manner

$$\begin{aligned}
a_{-2,\,-2}\dot{X}_{-2}+a_{-2,\,-1}\dot{X}_{-1}+a_{-2,\,0}\dot{X}_0+a_{-2,\,1}\dot{X}_1+a_{-2,\,2}\dot{X}_2 &= 0;\\
a_{-1,\,-2}\dot{X}_{-2}+a_{-1,\,-1}\dot{X}_{-1}+a_{-1,\,0}\dot{X}_0+a_{-1,\,1}\dot{X}_1+a_{-1,\,2}\dot{X}_2 &= 0;\\
a_{0,\,-2}\dot{X}_{-2}+a_{0,\,-1}\dot{X}_{-1}+a_{0,\,0}\dot{X}_0+a_{0,\,1}\dot{X}_1+a_{0,\,2}\dot{X}_2 &= 0;\\
a_{1,\,-2}\dot{X}_{-2}+a_{1,\,-1}\dot{X}_{-1}+a_{1,\,0}\dot{X}_0+a_{1,\,1}\dot{X}_1+a_{1,\,2}\dot{X}_2 &= 0;\\
a_{2,\,-2}\dot{X}_{-2}+a_{2,\,-1}\dot{X}_{-1}+a_{2,\,0}\dot{X}_0+a_{2,\,1}\dot{X}_1+a_{22}\dot{X}_2 &= 0.
\end{aligned} \tag{6.12}$$

According to what has been stated above, the coefficients in (6.12) are equal respectively to

$$a_{kk} = [A_0K(p)+D(p)]e^{(\lambda+jk\Omega)t};$$

$$a_{k,\,k+r} = \frac{1}{2}\,A_0m_re^{j\alpha_r}K(p)e^{(\lambda+jk\Omega)t}.$$

If, in expanding in a Fourier series the expressions for the coefficient $(\partial F(X)/\partial X)_{X=X(t)}$ we restrict ourselves to a finite number of terms, equal to ν, then all $a_{k,\,k+r}$ for $r>\nu$ reduce to zero. Thus, in connexion with reducing to zero a number of components, the system of equations (6.12) is made correspondingly simpler.

By equating to zero the determinant of the finite system of equations for the complex amplitudes, we obtain a polynomial with respect to λ with complex coefficients. The roots of this polynomial are equal to the values of λ required.

In order that the investigated periodic mode of operation be stable, it is necessary and sufficient that all $\mathrm{Re}(\lambda) < 0$. In order to investigate whether all λ satisfy the condition indicated, both algebraic and frequency criteria can be used.

Bearing in mind that here we are investigating the roots of a polynomial with complex coefficients, Shur's criterion can be employed in applying algebraic criteria of stability.

In using frequency methods, we can employ criteria, the analogue of known frequency criteria.

3. Calculation of the complete spectrum

On the basis of the methods developed in Chapter II above and in [6] we can obtain the characteristic equation in a finite form and, by employing frequency methods, we can solve problems of the stability of a periodic mode of operation, without having recourse to simplifications connected with the use of the hypothesis of an ideal filter.

Let us return to the equation (6.8). If we take into account that $D(p)\ \exp(\lambda + jk\Omega)t = D(\lambda + jk\Omega)\ \exp(\lambda + jk\Omega)t$ (where $p = d/dt$), then, by dividing all rows of the determinant of the system of equations (6.8) by $D(p)$, we obtain a new determinant, in which the diagonal element of the k-th row is equal to

$$1 + A_0 \frac{K(\lambda + jk\Omega)}{D(\lambda + jk\Omega)} \tag{6.13}$$

and a non-diagonal element is equal to

$$\frac{1}{2} A_0 m_r \times \frac{K(\lambda + jk\Omega)}{D(\lambda + jk\Omega)} . \tag{6.14}$$

Let us bear in mind that

$$\frac{K(\lambda+jk\Omega)}{D(\lambda+jk\Omega)} \to 0 \text{ for } \operatorname{Re}\lambda \to 0 \tag{6.15}$$

the degree of the polynomial $D(\lambda)$ being higher than the degree of the polynomial $K(\lambda)$.

Let the polynomial $D(p)$ have n different roots, r of which are simple and t are double, then the determinant obtained from the determinant of the system (6.12) by dividing all elements by $D(p)$ can be represented in a form similar to the determinant (2.6) [see, also, (2.7) and (2.8)].

By reducing the infinite determinant thus obtained to a finite form according to the formulae (2.14) and (2.15), we obtain, just as above for the case considered, a characteristic equation of the form

$$\sum_{i=1}^{r} \frac{D_i^{(1)}}{j\Omega} \cot\left[\frac{\pi}{j\Omega}(\lambda-\alpha j)\right] + \sum_{i=1}^{t} \frac{D_i^{(1)}}{j\Omega} \cot\left[\frac{\pi}{j\Omega} - \alpha_i)\right] - \\ - \sum_{i=1}^{t} \frac{D_i^{(2)}\pi^2}{\Omega^2 \sin^2\left[(\lambda-\alpha_i)\pi \frac{1}{j\Omega}\right]} = -1. \tag{6.16}$$

After the characteristic equation has been reduced to a finite form, we can use for the analysis of stability one of the known frequency criteria.

We shall take into account that the use of frequency criteria is distinguished here by certain original features. These are determined by the fact that in our case the characteristic equation is a periodic function of frequency. In this connection, as occurs for systems with amplitude-pulse modulation, it suffices to plot $\Delta(j\omega)$ for ω varying within the interval from $(-\Omega/2)$ to $(+\Omega/2)$.

Let us discuss briefly the application of Mikhailov's frequency criterion to a system of equations of motion for which the characteristic equation has the form

$$\sin^2\left[\pi(\lambda-\alpha_1)\frac{1}{j\Omega}\right] = \pi^2 D_1^{(2)} \frac{1}{\Omega^2}\,. \tag{6.17}$$

Let α_1 be a purely imaginary number. Then Mikhailov's plot of the left-hand side of the equation (6.17) will be a straight line coinciding with the real axis.

If α is either a real or a complex number, Mikhailov's plot of the left-hand side of (6.17) will be represented by an infinite number of ellipses situated in each other and passing in turn through all quadrants. For small values of the right-hand side of (6.17), i.e. for small values of D_1 and corresponding small values of the modulation parameter, Mikhailov's plot will traverse in turns all quadrants and the system will be stable. As the modulation depth increases, the right-hand side of (6.17) increases and the ellipse corresponding to the left-hand side of (6.17) is displaced to the right, and for a certain limit value of the modulation depth the system becomes unstable. The limit value of the modulation depth corresponding to the boundary of stability will be determined by the condition

$$\mathrm{Re}\left[\sin^2(j\omega_1-\alpha_1)\frac{\pi}{j\Omega}\right] = D_1^{(2)}\pi^2\frac{1}{\Omega^2}, \tag{6.18}$$

where $D_1^{(2)}$ depends on the modulation depth.

4. Remarks on the investigation of the stability of circuits with feedback containing parameters varying periodically (or exponentially)

The investigation of the stability of systems with a closed feedback loop, containing periodically varying parameters, can be carried out on the basis of the results obtained above.

Let us consider the procedure for applying the methods shown to the investigation of the stability of the system indicated. We shall distinguish two cases: (1) when the system is stable under open-loop conditions, (2) when the system is unstable under open-loop conditions.

In the first case, in a similar manner as is done for systems with constant parameters, we can use Nyquist's criterion.

In contrast, however, to systems with constant parameters, we cannot use here the concept of frequency characteristic of the transfer factor, since, as has already been pointed out, the response of the system in systems with variable parameters cannot be represented as the product of a transfer factor times the disturbance. Accordingly in the analysis of stability by means of Nyquist's criterion we have to employ here the transform of the system response to the disturbance applied. As is well-known, such a situation is met in control theory in the case of pulse systems, which are a particular case of systems with periodically or exponentially varying parameters.

We shall observe that, just as follows from Chapter III, the stability of a system with variable parameters *depends upon the form of the disturbance (in particular on its phase, in the case of a periodic disturbance)*.

If we agree that by stability of a system with variable parameters we mean its stability in the presence of a sinusoidal disturbance, then, as can be seen from formula (3.26), the transform of the response of the system with periodic parameters to a sinusoidal disturbance is a periodic (or exponential) function of frequency, expressed in terms of simple trigonometric (or hyperbolic) functions and, respectively, in the case of parameters varying according to an exponential law, in terms of hyperbolic functions.

Thus, in this case, the investigation by means of Nyquist's criterion can be carried out in the same manner as is usually done in the cases when the transform of the output response is a transcendental function (the case of a circuit with distributed constants, impulse circuits, etc.).

In this connection we shall distinguish here two possible cases: (1) the frequency characteristic is a periodic function of frequency, (2) the amplitude-frequency characteristic tends to zero as $\omega \to \infty$.

Let us use Nyquist–Mikhailov's criterion.

We shall proceed from Nyquist's criterion in the following form: "A closed-loop system is stable if the difference between the number of passages of the phase characteristic $\varphi(\omega)$ of the open-loop system through the lines π, 3π, . . . , in a downwards direction and the number of passages through these lines in an upwards direction, in all the regions of the graph in which the amplitude-frequency characteristic passes above the line $A(\omega) = 1$, is equal to $m/2$, where m is the number of the roots of the characteristic equation of the open-loop system with a positive real part."

In the case considered of a system stable under open-loop conditions, when the frequency characteristic is a periodic function of frequency, we restrict ourselves to plotting the amplitude-frequency and the phase-frequency characteristics in the interval from $\lambda = -j\Omega/2$ to $\lambda = j\Omega/2$, and, when the amplitude-frequency characteristic tends to zero, we restrict the plot of the characteristic up to that value of frequency after which, for a further increase of frequency, the condition $A(\omega) < 1$ is observed.

In the case of a system unstable under open-loop conditions the investigation can also be carried out in a similar manner. The difficulty here consists in the determination of the number of roots of the characteristic equation of the open-loop system that lie in the right-hand half-plane.

In this connexion, if the frequency characteristic is a periodic function of frequency the problem is simplified in that Nyquist's plot is plotted for a range of frequencies from $-\Omega/2$ to $+\Omega/2$ and accordingly we must find the number of stable roots for this same frequency range. This number will be finite for a system not containing distributed constants, namely it will not be greater than the number of roots of the characteristic equation of the part of the system considered not containing variable parameters.

In the case when the transform of the response of the system is not a periodic function of frequency, but the amplitude-frequency characteristic tends to zero as $\omega \to \infty$, the number of roots of the transfer function of the open-loop system that lie in the right-hand half-plane will be finite and can be determined on the basis of the formulae (3.25) and (3.26) proceeding from the known roots α_i of the characteristic equation of the part of the open-loop system not containing constant parameters.

5. Analysis of the stability of pulse circuits with feedback

The analysis of the stability of pulse circuits, just as the analysis of linear continuous circuits, can be carried by means of both analytical and graphical methods.

The use of analytical methods for investigating the stability of pulse circuits entails additional difficulties in comparison with the investigation of continuous circuits. These difficulties are determined by the fact that the transforms of the system functions of pulse circuits are transcendental functions of the operator p. The use of graphical methods for the analysis of stability, based on various frequency criteria, does not involve substantial additional difficulties in comparison with the usual application of these methods to the analysis of continuous linear circuits.

In this section we consider briefly certain features of the application of the main graphical methods for the analysis of stability in linear pulse circuits and also give a general idea of analytical methods.[10, 14, 18]

(a) The construction of Nyquist's diagram in the p-plane

The analytical method for the investigation of stability in the p-plane involves very laborious calculations, since even rejecting higher harmonics, the degree of the characteristic equation is raised several times. Calculations become particularly complicated in the cases when the function $\Delta(\lambda)$ contains λ to a high degree, i.e. in the case of a system with a large number of degrees of freedom. Under these conditions graphical methods based on various frequency criteria prove the most effective.

In particular, we can use here the well-known Nyquist–Mikhailov's criterion, enabling us to solve the problem of stability proceeding from the amplitude-phase characteristic of the transfer factor. In this connection, in the case of the simple control system considered above, for which the transfer factor was equal to

$$W(p) = \frac{K}{p(p+1)}, \tag{6.19}$$

we obtain

$$W^*(p) = \frac{1}{T} \sum_{n=-\infty}^{\infty} W(p+jn\omega). \tag{6.20}$$

By restricting ourselves to the first two terms in (6.20) and replacing, accordingly, $W^*(p)$ by the approximate expression

$$W^*(p) \cong \frac{1}{T}[W(p)+W(p-j\omega)] \tag{6.21}$$

by substituting $j\omega$ for p and letting ω vary from $\omega = 0$ to $\omega_{\text{per}}/2$, we can plot Nyquist's diagram. The approximation will be better, the closer the frequency characteristic $W(j\omega)$ is to the frequency characteristic of a low-pass filter [18].

(b) The construction of Nyquist's diagram on the basis of the z-transformation

As has been indicated above in introducing the z-transformation, the imaginary axis of the p-plane is transformed, as a result of the substitution $e^{pT} = z$, into the boundary of the circle of unit radius in the z-plane.

Accordingly, if we substitute in the vector $W(z)$ values of z lying on the circle of unit radius, the vector $W(z)$ will describe the same curve that the vector $W^*(p)$ would describe if p had been varied along the imaginary axis from $p = -j\infty$ to $p = +j\infty$.

The advantage of such an investigation in comparison with the approximate method described above is determined by the fact that here the need no longer arises to neglect terms of the frequency characteristic corresponding to higher frequencies, and all the investigation is based on exact expressions. Thus, even in the absence of a sharply defined cut-off frequency, the correctness of the results obtained remains certain, since the error, difficult to estimate, connected with the use of the approximation shown above, is avoided in the calculations.

As an example, we shall consider the same simple system with feedback as in the previous section. The z-transform of the transfer factor for this system is equal to[18]

$$W(z) = \frac{kz(1-e^{-T})}{(z-1)(z-e^{-T})}. \qquad (6.22)$$

If the pulser frequency is equal to $\omega = 4$ rad/sec, we have accordingly $T = 2\pi/\omega = \pi/2$ and $e^{-T} = 0.208$. The factor $W(z)$ will be equal to

$$W(z) = \frac{0.792\, kz}{(z-1)(z-0.208)}. \qquad (6.23)$$

The amplitude and phase of $W(z)$ is determined for a certain value of the frequency by the value of z which, in its turn, is determined by the position of the point on the boundary of the unit circle in the z-plane corresponding to the given value of frequency. For example, for an angular frequency of 1 rad/sec z is equal to

$$z = e^{j/T} = 1 \measuredangle 90° = e^{j1\frac{2\pi}{\omega}} = e^{j1\frac{2\pi}{4}} = e^{j\frac{\pi}{2}}. \qquad (6.24)$$

The corresponding value of $W(z)$ is determined by the equality

$$W(z) = \frac{0.792\, k\bar{A}}{\bar{B}\bar{C}}, \qquad (6.25)$$

where $\bar{A}$ is a vector drawn from the origin of the co-ordinates to the point $1 \measuredangle 90°$, $\bar{B}$ is a vector drawn from the point 1 to the point $1 \measuredangle 90°$, and $\bar{C}$ is a vector drawn from the point 0.208 to the point $1 \measuredangle 90°$. On the basis of a graphical construction we can obtain

$$Wj(1) = \frac{0.792k\,(1 \measuredangle 90°)}{(1.414 \measuredangle 135°)\,(1.0216 \measuredangle 101.8°)} =$$

$$= 0.86\frac{K}{T} \measuredangle -146.8°. \qquad (6.26)$$

By evaluating $W(z)$ for values of ω from $\omega = 0$ to $\omega = \omega_{per}/2$ we plot Nyquist's diagram.

Although such a construction is somewhat more complicated than the graphical summation needed in constructing the transfer locus from the approximate expression for $W^*(p)$, it has the great advantage of being rigorous. This advantage is determined by the fact that, although the separate terms neglected in the expression for $W^*(p)$ are small, their sum can have a considerable value in the absence of a sharply defined cut-off frequency.

The analysis of stability by means of Nyquist's diagram, independently of whether this has been constructed from an approximate expression for $W^*(p)$ or from the exact $W(z)$, is carried out in just the same manner as usual.

By considering Nyquist's diagram we can see that the effect of introducing a pulser leads to an increase of the phase shift for a given gain, i.e. to a decrease of the relative stability. Nyquist's diagram enables us to find directly the maximum achievable value of the gain, k/T, of a pulse control system. In the case considered $W(j2)$ can be increased up to 1, before stability fails. The maximum value of the gain will correspond to just this value.

If we restrict ourselves in $W^*(j\omega)$ to two terms only, the maximum value of K/T will be equal to 2.5; correspondingly, if $\omega_{per} = 4$ rad/sec, k will be equal to 3.93 as opposed to the exact value 3.05 found above.

REFERENCES

1. L. S. Gol'dfarb; On certain non-linearities in automatic-control systems, *Avtomat i Telemekh.*, No. 5 (1947).
2. M. A. Aizerman and I. M. Smirnova; On the use of the method of small parameters for investigating periodic modes of operation in automatic-control systems, *Sbornik pamyati A. A. Andronova (Collected Articles in commemoration of A. A. Andronov)*, Izd. Akad. Nauk SSSR (1955).
3. M. A. Aizerman; *Lektsii po teorii avtomaticheskogo regulirovaniya (Lectures on Automatic Control Theory)*, Moscow, GTTI (1956 – 58).
4. V. A. Taft: On the stability of automatic control systems in the presence in them of an ideal linear filter. *Avtomat. i Telemekh.*, No. 7 (1958).
5. V. A. Taft; *Elektricheskiye tsepi s periodicheski izmenyayushchimisya parametrami i perekhodnyye protsessy v sinkhronnykh mashinakh (Electrical circuits with periodically varying parameters and transient processes in synchronous machines)*, Izd. Akad. Nauk SSSR (1958).
6. V. A. Taft; On the analysis of stability of periodic modes of operation in non-linear automatic-control systems, *Avtomat. i telemekh.*, No. 9 (1959).
7. V. A. Taft; On the frequency characteristics of two-pole and four-pole networks containing variable periodically-varying parameters (to be published).
8. E. T. Whittaker and G. N. Watson; *Course of Modern Analysis* (transl.), Moscow, GTTI (1937).
9. Z. B. Ryzhik and I. S. Gradshtein; *Tablitsy summ, integralov, proizvedenii (Tables of Sums, Integrals and Products)*, Moscow, GTTI (1954).
10. Ya. Z. Tsypkin; *Teoriya impul'snykh sistem (Theory of Pulse Systems)* Fizmatgiz (1959). English translation by Pergamon Press, Oxford (1963), under the title *Sampling Systems Theory.*
11. E. A. Meyerovich; Calculation of transients in complex electrical circuits, *Izv. Akad. Nauk SSSR otdel. tekh. nauk,* No. 10 (1950).
12. E. A. Meyerovich and V. A. Taft; Engineering methods of calculation of non-steady-state processes in complex electrical circuits, *Elektrichestvo*, No. 8 (1952).

13. D. D. Ivanenko and A. A. Sokolov; *Klassicheskaya teoriya polya (Classical Field Theory)*, Moscow, GTTI (1949).
14. V. V. Solodovnikov; *Osnovy avtomaticheskogo regulirovaniya (Fundamentals of Automatic Control)*, Mashgiz (1959). English translation by Pergamon Press, Oxford (1963).
15. G. P. Tartakovskii; The stability of linear circuits with variable parameters, *Radiotekhnika i elektronika 2*, No. 1 (1957).
16. J. R. Ragazzini and L. A. Zadeh; The analysis of pulse systems, *Trans. AIEE, 71*, part II (1952).
17. A. R. Bergen and J. R. Ragazzini, Sampled-data processing techniques for feedback control systems, *Trans. AIEE, 73*, part II (1954).
18. Truxal; Synthesis of Control Systems, New York (1955).
19. L. Zadeh; Circuit analysis of linear varying-parameter networks, *J. appl. Phys. 21*, No. 11 (1950).

INDEX